Robert

2. 1

R.A.Whitehead

GARRETT WAGONS

Part 3
Electrics & Motors

R.A.Whitehead & Partners

Tonbridge,
Kent

1996

Fig.1. *No.33119 (later referred to as No.101), the first Garrett electric to be built,*
delivered to the Great Eastern Railway in Norwich, May 14, 1917.

Published by R.A.Whitehead & Partners
42 Hadlow Road
Tonbridge, Kent TN9 1NZ

Photographs: Unless otherwise acknowledged all illustrations are from the collections of the now defunct firm of Richard Garrett Engineering Ltd., or of the author. Illustrations from other sources are acknowledged individually.

Cover: Group of Garrett trolley buses outside the depot of Nordsjøellands Elektricitets og Spørvejs Aktieselkab soon after delivery in late Summer, 1926.

Typeset in Times New Roman 10 by J.E.Whitehead.

Printed and bound by Biddles Ltd., Woodbridge Park, Guildford, GU1 1DA

ISBN 0-9508298-7-0

Contents

Fig.2.   *Modern methods in an ambience of squalor as Glasgow Corporation's GTZ refuse collector No.5 (Works No.347) is loaded in a tenement street in South side Glasgow.*

Fig. 3. *O-type trolley bus No.310, built in 1926 and bodied by Strachan & Brown of Acton, London, W.5 for operation in the suburbs of Copenhagen by Nordsjøellands Elektricitets og Spørvejs Aktieselkab, who rebuilt the body as shown in 1950. Withdrawn early in the 1960's, it was repatriated and is now the property of the East Anglia Transport Museum, Carlton Colville.*   [East Anglia Transport Museum]

Foreword

by K.C. Blacker Esq. MCIT

I am grateful to have been asked to contribute a foreword to this last volume in Bob Whitehead's trilogy dealing with the story of the wagons built by Garretts of Leiston. A lifetime spent working in transport has been enriched, for me, by a keen interest in the history of the industry and in the thrill that opening new avenues of knowledge through research into aspects of its past can bring. Although road transport, in its mechanised form, is comparatively recent in origin, having been mostly a twentieth century phenomenon, a surprisingly large amount of detail as to its explosive growth and development has already been lost or forgotten. In this book we have a rare, in-depth account of how one small firm played its role in manufacturing for the transport industry; of how its commercial decisions spanned the whole range between extreme conservatism and extraordinary vision; and how, in the face of pressure from larger, better funded competitors, it struggled and lost.

The little town of Leiston, situated in a quiet corner of rural Suffolk, seems an unlikely location for a major engineering works. Today, when the manufacturing of road vehicles is only feasible on a quantity basis to keep down unit costs, it seems inconceivable that a works such as Garretts could have built road vehicles by the hundreds. Such were the engineering skills within the works that steam wagons, trolleybuses, threshing machines, water turbines and even ice cream freezers could all be manufactured, plus much more besides. However Garrett's failure to emulate its competitors by concentrating its activities and its limited resources on a smaller range of improved quality products selling at lower prices must undoubtedly have contributed to its undoing.

One of Garrett's strong points was its ability to define and respond to new circumstances, such as those which led it into the realms of battery electric van manufacturing and ultimately to trolleybuses. The development and production of both are fully described in this volume and we also learn how, despite reasonable sales figures, the Garrett firm failed to achieve adequate profitability on them and was forced to bow to stronger competitors. We also learn of Garrett's disastrous attempt at establishing a range of petrol lorries 'on the cheap' which resulted in the Caledon fiasco, and of its later, ill-fated endeavours to develop internal combustion-engined lorries. It is a little remembered fact that Garrett was the very first in this country to build a lorry powered by a diesel engine from new.

Through having access to Garrett's records, the author has been able to produce a very thorough history of the Company, enhanced by acquaintance with members of the Garrett family and former employees. This combination of documentary evidence with first hand personal recollections enables us to learn about many of the personalities involved and about their struggles at board room level and elsewhere. We also encounter some of the trials and tribulations which the Garrett team had to overcome such as their difficulties over the first electric wagon trials in Norwich, the problems with Mexborough's first batch of trolleybuses, the horrendous mechanical failures of the 1931 oil-engined lorry, and the subterfuge employed to allow the first GTZ dust cart to pass its acceptance trials. Few transport historians are fortunate enough to obtain access to such detailed material or to add as much 'flesh' to the 'bones' of the story as in this case.

I suspect that I may be a few years younger than the author, and thus I have no personal recollection of Garrett's electric vehicles in service except, of course, for the famous Glasgow dust carts which lasted well into the post-war era. However, I have a personal interest in Garrett electrics because the East Anglia Transport Museum at Carlton Colville, Lowestoft, of which I am a director, possesses what is believed to be the only one still in working order, in the shape of a Copenhagen trolleybus. It is sad so little remains, but still the memory lingers on.

Ken Blacker
Blundeston, Suffolk

March, 1996

Preface

Questioners with the benefit of seventy or eighty years of hindsight have often said to me 'Why did not the Garretts realise in sufficient time that the day of the steam engine was ending and that it was necessary to develop alternative products?' Whereas in Parts 1 and 2 of this trilogy I have given an account of the development of the overtype and undertype *steam* wagons produced by the company, in this final volume it is hoped to set out the story of the electric and motor vehicles which they built. This narrative may, therefore, demonstrate that the necessity for change *was* understood on the Board of Richard Garrett & Sons Ltd. and that consideration of alternatives to steam as a prime mover took place at a relatively early stage. In 1913-14 when such discussions began seriously, my late friend Victor Garrett was not a director of the firm but, of course, knew from family contacts what the contemplated developments were. Three years later he did become a director and from that time onward was directly involved in the formulation of the various projects. Whereas Alfred, the second Garrett brother, had no pronounced opinions on technical matters, being by nature an administrator, Stephen, the third brother, was rated by Victor as the most innovative in many ways. He evinced the greatest interest in the internal combustion engine whilst the eldest brother, Frank, believed that electric traction had a bright future. As events are now shaping it may yet turn out that he was ultimately right, but in the shorter term Stephen's advocacy of the motor engine might have been the more commercially advantageous policy.

A few motor tractors were actually constructed before all these debates were cut short by the outbreak of war in August, 1914, which took away from the Works both Frank and Stephen Garrett, the latter being killed at Neuve Chapelle the following year. Thus this cruel stroke of fate settled the way in which the firm would view alternative propulsion for some years ahead. Frank Garrett was invalided out of the Army in 1915 and picked up the investigations into electric vehicle manufacture which had not been pursued in his absence.

With the perception conferred by hindsight, the AGE combine which Garretts joined in 1919 can be seen to have been a poorly managed organisation, not well constituted initially, and begun in an atmosphere of excessive optimism that changed, once circumstances demonstrated that it could not be sustained, to an almost diametrically opposite attitude of pessimism and penny-pinching. This latter meant that many good ideas seeded within the group did not yield the growth they seemed to promise. Nevertheless, there were scores of stalwart characters in the constituent companies whose devotion to the projects in hand, together with their loyalty and integrity, makes what seems to me to be a story worth telling.

Tonbridge, Kent   Robert A.Whitehead
March, 1996

Acknowledgements and Thanks

The assembling of the information for this book was begun some thirty-five years ago. Because of this it is inevitable that a large number of those whom I have to thank must be referred to in the past tense. The most senior of these was the late Victor R.Garrett, the last family director of the Works to have survived, and an invaluable source of information on the reasons behind directorial decisions. I am also greatly indebted to those who successively had charge of the Works during the period of my researches: the late Alfred R.King, Reginald J.Hadfield, and Michael Hilton. Other directors who gave valuable help were Frank Andrews, Ernest Cuthbert, and Reginald Clarke, all now dead, the latter of whom became a valued personal friend.

The drawing office staff were also very helpful, especially Leslie W.Farrow, chief designer for much of this time, and his deputy, Arthur Woodhead. The late Frank Waddell, latterly editor of the *Leiston Observer,* was a draughtsman in the thresher department, which was responsible for wagon and bus bodies. He had known either as colleagues or as fellow townsmen most of the draughtsmen who had worked upon the vehicles. The late Herbert R. (Jack) Simpson gave much help as did, also, the late Arthur Pipe. My friend of many years, the late Edward C.Dunn, gave immense help in locating records and documents, and with personal reminiscence of the people involved. George Hambling, Walter Hall, and Geoffrey Marreco, all now dead, also contributed a great deal of practical information. Other individuals, not connected with the Works, who provided information were John Langford and Frank Willis.

Others who have been very helpful are the staffs of the National Motor Museum, Beaulieu; the Rural History Centre, Reading; the Library of the Institution of Mechanical Engineers; the County Records Office of Suffolk County Council; the Long Shop Museum, Leiston, (particularly David Williamson); and the Cleansing Department in Glasgow.

Valuable help was given by my son-in-law, Michael J.Walters, who did much research, and also read, commented upon and contributed to the manuscript. He prepared the list of vehicles in the Appendices. My wife, Jean, contributed a share beyond measure and without complaint to the twenty years or so of research we put in at Leiston works and about fifteen years elsewhere, besides editing the manuscript and setting it into type. Over the years Barry Finch gave much help in copying old photographs.

To all those named above I extend my heartfelt and most sincere thanks as well as to all those who have contributed but whom consideration of space precludes from individual mention.

I am especially grateful to Ken Blacker for his kindness in reading and commenting upon the manuscript, drawing upon his copious experience of buses of all types, both motor and electric, and for the encouragement he has given to the project by agreeing to contribute the foreword.

Bibliography - Parts 1, 2, & 3

The information contained in these three volumes was, in the main, extracted from documents that existed at Leiston Works. Other sources that were consulted included the periodicals:

Commercial Motor   *Engineer*   *Implement & Machinery Review*
Motor Traction   *Engineering*   *Trolleybus Magazine*
Tramway & Railway World
and the books: *The Electric Trolleybus* [R.A.Bishop, published 1930 by Pitman, London]
                 British Trolleybus Systems [J.Joyce, J.S.King, A.G.Newman, published 1986 by Ian Allan, Shepperton]

Other books by R.A.Whitehead
¶ denotes still in print

The Story of the Colne Valley (jointly with F.D.Simpson)	Oakwood Press [Reprint]
Garretts of Leiston	Percival Marshall
A Century of Service	Eddison Plant
The Age of the Traction Engine	Ian Allan
A Century of Steam Rolling	Ian Allan
Steam in the Village	David & Charles
Garrett 200	Transport Bookman
Kaleidoscope of Steam Wagons	Marshall Harris & Baldwin
Kaleidoscope of Traction Engines	Marshall Harris & Baldwin
Wallis & Steevens - a History	R.L.S.
¶ *A Review of Steam Tractors*	R.L.S.
¶ *Austrian Steam Locomotives 1837-1981*	R.A.Whitehead & Partners
¶ *The Beloved Coast & the Suffolk Sandlings*	Terence Dalton
¶ *Jesse Ellis & the Maidstone Wagons*	R.A.Whitehead & Partners
¶ *Steam is the Essence*	R.A.Whitehead & Partners
¶ *Garrett Diesel Tractors*	R.A.Whitehead & Partners
¶ *Made by Garretts*	R.A.Whitehead & Partners
¶ *Garrett Wagons Part 1 - Pioneers & Overtypes*	R.A.Whitehead & Partners
¶ *Garrett Wagons Part 2 - Undertypes*	R.A.Whitehead & Partners

Fig.4. The first wagon delivered to a customer after serious production was begun in 1919 was No.102 for Blackpool Corporation's Electricity Department. Its duties included carrying tramway rails, hence the crane by Chatteris Engineering Co. Ltd. with which it was equipped.

Fig.5. Wagon No.112 (March 24, 1920) was a No.4 and was delivered to Eastern Counties Farmers in a smart grey livery. The wagon survived long enough to be converted to pneumatic tyres.

Fig. 6. (below). The Midland Railway took delivery of No.5 wagon No.121 as a chassis in May, 1920, and built this impressive, and heavy, body upon it. It was intended for use by the Hotels Department and spent some time at Bradford.

Chapter 1

In the Beginning

An aura of uncertainty, fostered to a large extent by the firm's own publications, pervaded the various accounts of when Richard Garrett & Sons Ltd. first embarked on the designing and building of battery powered electric vehicles. When they compiled their catalogue No.604 in 1925 they stated on page 3 that they had designed and produced in 1914 a 1½-ton electric vehicle 'which is still giving most excellent and economical service'. By the time catalogue No.652 came to be written in 1929 the story had changed. In it they stated, seemingly without a blush, that 'In 1911 we designed and constructed one of the first Electric Battery Vehicles ever built in this country'. Although I had unlimited access to the firm's records for about twenty years and knew members of the owning family, no trace of these legendary vehicles of 1911 and 1914 ever came to light. Neither of these assertions is correct.

The nearest we are likely to get to the facts is the information contained in the preliminary paragraphs of a confidential memorandum written by Col. Frank Garrett to members of the board of directors in July, 1921, the main section of which relates to matters dealt with in Chapter 2 where it is again referred to. The subject of his memorandum is a meeting he had on July 7, 1921, with Monnot, managing director of Edison Accumulators Ltd. and of the newly set up Edison subsidiary, Electricars Ltd:

> I was in touch with him in the summer of 1914 and, when War broke out, had an agreement ready to place before my Board with Edison's Accumulators Ltd., of which he was Managing director, for the sole agency of the Edison Battery for England and the Colonies. When I returned to business early in 1916 [sic] I again got in touch with Mr. Monnot and found he had already got to work with Arrol Johnson, and that for the time there was nothing doing. I again got in touch with him, but owing to some slackness on the part of our Sales, and my time being fully occupied on aeroplanes and munitions, this opportunity was again lost, and Mr. Monnot finally brought out Electricars Ltd. I called upon him again about two months ago to see if I could possibly persuade him to give us a chance of orders for chassis, as our original design and mechanical efficiency was worked to from particulars and accumulated experiences of the American trade, given to us by him.

He went on to refer to Monnot's having been particularly against the two motor *front* drive, which in 1914 was used by Norddeutsche Lloyd in Bremen and later was to be used by Ransomes, which he (Monnot) called 'a freak car which America had given up'. Thus, while the intention existed in 1914 to build battery electrics, following Monnot's advice, actual beginnings dated from the return of Colonel Frank Garrett from the Army in 1915, after Stephen Garrett had been killed in action, and could be said to start with the appointment of C.D.Cuppleditch as electric vehicle designer in the Spring of 1915.

His first design was a 3-ton wagon, the drawings for which were completed about mid-June, 1915, and summarized in drawing list No.176, but manufacture was not put in hand. At that time the Works was heavily preoccupied with the setting up of the lines for shell manufacture and there was, in all probability, no available capacity for new manufactures. Notwithstanding this, Cuppleditch was directed to continue with the second type of wagon envisaged, a 5-ton design, which occupied him until late November, 1915. These drawings were summarized in drawing list No.181, dated November 23, 1915. By this stage of the War there was an embargo upon the initiation of new development work on civilian projects, and it was deemed expedient, therefore, to let it be thought that the experiment had been in progress for some while longer than was actually the case.

It was decided to build this second and larger design of wagon, and work was commenced, as far as can now be judged, early in 1916. The demands of the armed forces had begun to produce a shortage of sound draught horses and of the fodder on which to keep them, thereby creating an interest among urban horse users - such as the railway town delivery services - in alternative means of motive power. Since motors were also in demand for the forces and, in any case, they depended upon imported fuel, this created an interest in electrics. In this atmosphere Garretts attracted the attention of the Great Eastern Railway to the electric they had in hand. How this happened is not known exactly. Col. Garrett's personal friendship with 'Young Tom' Aveling who, in turn, was a friend of Archibald McConochie, the jam and pickle maker, who was also a director of the Great Eastern might explain the connection. On the other hand it might simply have been the result of the operation of the wartime seller's market. Whatever the way in which the order was obtained, it stimulated work on the production of patterns and castings which hitherto had proceeded as the opportunity offered, and a beginning was made in obtaining the proprietary items required for the vehicle, but progress was relatively slow.

The original enquiry from the railway was for a 5-tonner to work in London but during the protracted period of building this was revised to a 3½-tonner for work in Norwich. The work of erecting took place in a corrugated iron lean-to shed against the south wall of the boiler shop with no crane or proper lifting facilities. The erector was Walter Rogers, a steam wagon erector of immense experience, and his helper was a young apprentice named Walter Hall who, after the conclusion of his apprenticeship, became first an erector, then a charge-hand and, later, a travelling service inspector. Walter Rogers had died before I first went to Leiston but I did get to know Walter Hall quite well.

The components used in this first wagon were dictated, no doubt, largely by what could be obtained on reasonable delivery. The chassis was constructed on the Works using standard rolled steel channels, with rivetted joints. The wheels were of cast steel with cruciform section spokes, and designed for solid rubber tyres. The dead rear axle and the front axle were probably obtained from the Kirkstall Forge Co. Ltd. in Leeds. Final drive was by twin Coventry roller chains from a countershaft incorporating the differential. The motor was placed transversely beneath the chassis with primary drive to the countershaft by a further Coventry chain. The bodywork consisted of a flat platform with chock rails. A narrow wooden cab was fitted with the roof inclined towards the rear, and curved on plan at the front. A simple curved sheet apron was fitted in front of the driver which provided some degree of protection but the cab as a whole was narrow and cramped. The driving position was more or less central, in this respect resembling the French Purrey steam wagon. The hand brake lever was on the right of the driver. The steering gear used was by Marles. The controller came from Crompton of Chelmsford. The Chloride batteries were located in a battery tray beneath the front end of the platform.

Despite the slow deliveries of parts and other set-backs the wagon was completed and ready for road testing in the autumn of 1916 which was done, as was customary with steam wagons, over the undulating road to Aldeburgh. On December 4 both it and its designer were deposited in Norwich, the former at the Great Eastern Railway Goods Depot and the latter at the Hotel Cecil in Thorpe Road, late and, as his journal discloses, disgruntled at having missed his train connection at Haddiscoe. At Norwich the wagon was to be subjected to 'in service' testing to the approval of Mr. W.Lincoln, the manager of the Goods Station, who was handling the electric vehicle experiment on behalf of the District Superintendent. It was to his office, therefore, that Cuppleditch made his way on arrival. Lincoln first showed him the Norwich Power Station at which the wagon was to be charged and then took him to the Victoria Goods Station from which it was to work on selected delivery rounds.

On December 5 Cuppleditch took the wagon to the Goods Station loading bank at 7.10 where it was loaded with two tons of mixed goods for delivery round the city by the Great Eastern carter allocated to it. It returned empty at 9.50 when a break for a late breakfast was taken. A second load of 2 tons 11cwt 5lbs took the carter until 11.25 to load, and they then set off round the outer parts of Norwich, including Mousehold Heath, on softer roads and up some steep hills, getting back to the Goods Station just before 1.30. The third run of the day took in more stiff gradients and several yards in what Cuppleditch called 'disgraceful condition', five inches deep in mud. The load on setting out was 2tons 17cwt. Back empty at 4.40 they again reloaded with 2 tons 3cwt, and set off round some of the hillier parts of the city finishing at the Power Station at 6.40. By this time Cuppleditch was getting to know his companion and asked him how the day with the wagon compared with a day with horses. Dye, the carter, said the tonnage they had moved exceeded what would have been done with three horses. He added that taking the load up Mousehold would have overtaxed horses or, as he put it 'To take a horse up there with a load many times would do it in'. The day's mileage was 18.5. Cuppleditch added a footnote to his letter of report to the Works to say he was transferring to the Great Eastern Hotel, the Hotel Cecil not being, it seems, up to scratch. The testing went on daily, except Sundays, until Saturday, December 23. On the Monday and Tuesday no work was done, as Cuppleditch complained, 'on account of the business houses being closed for Christmas holidays', and even on December 27 they did only two trips for the same reason. Cuppleditch obviously felt this to be slack and self indulgent.

The wagon had a spell at Victoria Station followed by one at Thorpe. Dye proved a good pupil and soon picked up the elements of wagon driving. The tonnages moved daily went up as he got used to the wagon but Cuppleditch noted that time was lost unnecessarily during loading as Dye had to sort and load the packages himself. As the trials progressed the foremen and staff became increasingly enthusiastic about the wagon and did all they could to help up the daily tonnage, realising that their chances of being allowed to retain it were likely to be enhanced if it appeared to be a money-saver. In the early days of the tests one or two hiccups occurred at the Power Station over the battery charging. During the night of December 6/7 the staff forgot to charge up the batteries at all, and Cuppleditch had to do his best to get two days work out of one charge. Full of contrition the Power Station men offered to give the batteries a boost during the dinner hour but, either in haste or ignorance, they put the charging leads on the wrong way and took out 20 ampere/hours before the fuse blew, stopping further loss. Fortunately Cuppleditch, arriving back soon after that, refixed the leads correctly, thereby getting enough boost to finish the day's work. He reported to the Works: 'This mistake was made on account of a change in the staff and I do not think it will occur again', from which remark one infers he must have expressed himself quite forcibly.

The tonnage handled by the wagon under Dye's care rose steadily, helped by the fact that, following railway standard carting practice, they often picked up as well as set down goods. The daily distances run remained relatively small, sometimes as low as nine and seldom more than fifteen miles, but finally, during the week ending January 14, 1917, the weekly tonnage handled exceeded 100 tons for the first time. Lincoln told Cuppleditch that the London management were pleased with the results obtained and that he was certain something would come out of it. Words cost nothing, and, regrettably, nothing came of those particular words. The Great Eastern bought that wagon but did not purchase any others.

Cuppleditch stayed on at Norwich until mid-January when he handed over responsibility for the wagon to Dye - by then a thoroughly competent driver - with whom Cuppleditch seems to have got on well. It continued in use at Norwich until mid-March, 1918, when it was sent to Ipswich in place of a 2½ ton Orwell electric wagon (built by Ransomes, Sims & Jefferies), which, in turn, went to Norwich to replace the Garrett. The Great Eastern Railway were clearly making an effort to evaluate which of the wagons best suited their needs, and a swap of this kind tended to eliminate or, at any rate, reduce the chance of operators being partisan in their reporting. No.33119 began work at Ipswich on March 12 under a driver named Holden who had previously had the Orwell.

The Crompton controller fitted to the wagon was probably the least satisfactory of the bought-in components. By contrast the batteries, from the Chloride Electric Storage Co. of Clifton Junction, Manchester, seem to have given little trouble. On the Saturday after the wagon arrived in Ipswich Cuppleditch and an unnamed fitter took the train to Ipswich armed with sundry spare parts for the controller. When the wagon finished work about 3.0 p.m. they completely dismantled the controller; cleaned, trimmed up and smoothed off the copper drum; serviced the contact fingers and generally set it to rights. This seemed to produce an improvement. On a visit to it in July Cuppleditch was surprised to encounter Dye, the Norwich driver, who was on holiday in Ipswich and had actually driven the Garrett on a few of its delivery trips. Dye told Cuppleditch he would have liked to have the wagon back at Norwich partly, one supposes, because it was altogether a bigger and heavier wagon, capable of taking loads substantially in excess of its 3½ ton rating. He was not to know, of course, that it had been designed originally as a 5-tonner. On this visit Cuppleditch found that the steering drop arm was loose. When he returned on August 19 with the new drop arm he was greeted with the cheering news that the controller again 'required looking at'.

This was, indeed, the truth. Upon being opened up the controller was found to be badly burned, in one or two cases to such an extent that the contactor finger could not make proper contact, whilst in the most extreme instance a hole had been burned through the copper drum allowing the fifth speed contact to fall out. The hole had been fudged up with a brass strip, and Cuppleditch found that this was short circuiting the fifth and sixth speeds. In his report he summed up his thoughts on the cause of the trouble with the controller:

The design of our speed changing gear is such that it allows the driver to place the controller between speeds, the finger thus being, in some cases, half on and half off the contacts and in others causing local short circuits. Heavy current density is thus caused; and [upon] the drum being moved so that the contacts are just clear of the fingers, an arc occurs which has a very serious effect.

He commented that it would be possible to remove this spark entirely from the controller drum by placing in circuit a switch with a quick break and a magnetic blow-out which would have had the effect of localising all sparks to the switch, a considerable improvement since it was much easier to detach and clean the latter than it was to dismantle the controller.

Doubtless the type of controller used had been dictated, at least in part, by what could be obtained in the face of wartime shortages, but in writing of the design in such an Olympian fashion he was somewhat overlooking or shrugging off the fact that he had been the designer. During 1917 he had produced drawings for a revised version of the No.5 wagon, summarized in drawing list No.209 and completed on October 10, 1917. This he had followed by a set of drawings for a No.4 electric wagon (list No.224, July 24, 1918) and a No.3 wagon (list No.225 of the same date). In these a Vickers controller was specified. Cromptons had not distinguished themselves in the design of the controller, and had compounded their unpopularity by a thoroughly bodged repair executed to it by one of their fitters in the Spring of 1919. The trouble with the controller undoubtedly weighed against No.33119 when the Great Eastern Railway came to evaluate it. Another thing that told against it was the lightness of the Coventry roller chains between the transversely placed motor and the rear drive sprockets, whilst the cramped dimensions of the cab and the inadequate shelter thus provided were noted with disfavour. These points were taken care of in Cuppleditch's revised designs.

Who supplied the motor in the first vehicle is not known for certain. It seems to have given no trouble at any time. This, too, may have been a Crompton product but on the other hand it is possible that it was a Vickers, as used in the subsequent first production vehicles. The front wheels first fitted to the wagon were not satisfactory, though what the problems were is not known. A new pair of wheels (to drawing EV16402) complete with tyres was made and sent in August, 1917. The rear tyres fared rather better but by Autumn, 1918, needed renewal. They had probably covered some 7 000 miles by that time, not too bad a mileage, but they had become very tatty by the time of renewal. After his visit on November 4, 1918, Cuppleditch remarked in his report: 'The rear tyres are just about at their last gasp'. The railway company had ordered new tyres which were expected that week but seem to have run into trouble fitting them as the wheels were sent in December to Leiston Works where the ribs were turned off the rims and the new twin 110 mm x 771mm tyres were pressed on.

The wagon suffered from well-intentioned but inept adjustments, bodged repairs and uninformed maintenance. After its arrival in Ipswich Cuppleditch noted that whilst the offside chain was slack that on the nearside was, as he put it, 'as tight as a violin string'. On another of his visits to Ipswich the footbrake was reported to him as 'working stiffly'. He found that the cross shaft carrying the levers had seized up at one end because of lack of oil. He went on:

> The holes provided for oil were full of dirt. considerable work was entailed in freeing this shaft as it was too tight to be moved by hand, a tommy bar had to be used. A loose lever on the shaft, which allows the equaliser bar to operate, was also corroded rigidly to the shaft and had to be freed by levering backwards and forwards with tommy bars.

On August 19, 1918, he investigated a complaint that the footbrake would not hold. He discovered that the driver had been adjusting the brakes and had tightened up one side turnbuckle but had forgotten to lock it with the lock nuts thus allowing it to slacken off.

To prevent a recurrence of the oiling problems on the brake cross shaft Cuppleditch substituted grease cups on the designs he had on his board for post-war production. The cab was enlarged and the layout was altered to give the driver greater freedom of movement; Vickers controllers replaced the Crompton type; and heavier driving chains were fitted. None of these impending changes influenced the G.E.R. management in their decision as to whether future orders should be for Garrett wagons or Orwells from Ransomes, Sims & Jefferies. A rather curious report, of which Garretts were given a copy, was the basis of their decision. The reasoning it contained is so odd as to be worth setting out. It stated that whereas , at both Ipswich and Norwich, the Garrett (a 3½-tonner) and the Orwell (a 2½-tonner) had, within very narrow margins, moved the same average daily tonnage, the Orwell had run more miles to do it (actually an average of 17.5 miles per day compared with 11.5 for the Garrett). This was accounted to be in the Orwell's favour. As the report put it:

> This is distinctly in favour of the ORWELL vehicle as in the event of the mileages having been equal, more short distance journeys could have been made and therefore more tonnage dealt with.

It seems not to have occurred to the author of the report that as the result of each load on the Garrett having been larger, the number of journeys and hence the dead mileage between first and last calls and the depot might have been reduced, nor that the loads carried were governed by the work available at the respective depots. Nevertheless, whatever one may think of the reasoning in the report its advice was followed, and as a result the G.E.R. adopted Orwell wagons rather than Garretts.

The experience Cuppleditch had gained from monitoring his wagon's career in practical work had, however, been of great value both to him and to the firm, and the results appear in the next chapter.

Fig.7. Yet another railway customer to buy a bare chassis was the North Staffordshire, based in Stoke-on-Trent. No.120 (March, 1920) was equipped with characteristically heavy railway bodywork.

Fig.8. *(below)* Weston & Westall had two identical No.4 (2½ ton) wagons, Nos.115 and 117. This is No.115. The platforms were of sandwich construction with a lead tray to prevent salt penetrating to the chassis, doubtless effective but very heavy.

Fig.10. (right) No.4 type (Works No.133) supplied to E.C.Robson & Sons through the agency of Christy Bros., Chelmsford, in September, 1920.

Fig.9. *(left)* Despite its massive looks No.109 was only meant to carry 1½ tons. Supplied to Boots Pure Drug Co. Ltd. as a bare chassis it had body and cab added by its purchasers.

Fig.11. Wagon No.146 was a No.5 (3½-tonner) completed in September, 1920, as a demonstration vehicle. Although lettered and lined in the style of the London & North Western Railway, it was only with them on trial and was not purchased.

Fig.12. No.3 type, No.111, one of five ordered by the Great Northern, Great Central & Great Eastern Railways, probably for their joint parcel service in Lincoln. The order was cancelled halfway through and the wagon, fitted with the narrow cab shown to enable long baulks of timber to be carried, was sold to Jewson & Son, the Norwich timber merchants.

Chapter 2

The Electric Wagons in Production

At some date after the completion of No.33119 the decision was taken to allocate Works numbers to electric vehicles in a separate sequence to those used for steam engines. No.33119 was accorded the honorary position of first in the series and was referred to in the register of electrics as No.101although it probably never actually carried that number.

When serious production of electric wagons began after the Armistice of 1918 the first to be produced was a No.5 for a 3½ ton load (Works No.102), updated as noted in the preceding chapter. The most conspicuous external evidence of this was in the design of the cab which, though rudimentary by modern standards, was much wider, provided with doors, and fitted with a larger but still rounded apron. This wagon, fitted with an end-tipping body and a crane, was for use by Blackpool Corporation Electricity Department to whom it was delivered on August 1, 1919. The motor used was a Vickers. The battery equipment was a 44 cell Ironclad Exide IMV9. This was followed by a second No.5, taking the Works No.106, which was sent to Morgans Brewery Co. Ltd. in Norwich on October 23, 1919. The remaining production in 1919 consisted of two No.3 (1½ ton) and three No.4 (2½ton) wagons, two of which, Nos.103 and 104 for the Lancashire & Yorkshire Railway Co., were actually not delivered until early in the New Year. The other, No.105, was despatched to its purchasers, Siddall & Hilton of Sowerby Bridge, West Riding, on September 20, 1919. Why the delivery of the two for the Lancashire & Yorkshire Railway was thus delayed is not recorded, but was probably connected with the railway company's inspection and acceptance procedures. In the No.4 wagon many components were interchangeable with the No.5. Keeping down unladen weight has a pronounced effect upon the operating *economics* of most vehicles but in the electric vehicle it is critical also to the mileage achieved from each battery charge. Thus, although standardisation was praiseworthy in many cases, it was achieved in this instance at the expense of adding weight, probably against Cuppleditch's advice, and certainly to the detriment of performance. The smaller vehicle had virtually the same chassis as the larger, the same wheels (albeit with 20mm less width of tyre to each wheel), and the same countershaft, axles and steering. The No.4 had an I.M.V.7 battery instead of an I.M.V.9, saving 4¾ cwt., and a 50 volt instead of a 60 volt motor, but with an all-up weight of 86 cwt. compared with 95 cwt. on the larger vehicle there was a weight difference of only 9 cwt., two-thirds of which was accounted for by the battery, motor, and tyres. In the case of the No.3 wagon, carrying 1½ tons, the comparison made the design seem even less logical. The motor was identical with the No.4; only the battery (reduced to I.M.V.6) and the tyres (again reduced in width by 20mm per wheel) showed any significant change. The unladen weight of the No.3 was 260% of the payload; of the No.4, 172%; and of the No.5 only 136%. Cuppleditch had earlier had an opportunity to have a close look at an American G.V. electric wagon operated by Tibbenhams in Ipswich, the chassis of which he had noted as being of much lighter construction than those used at Garretts, which were mostly of standard section steel channel. The exceptions among the early electrics were some of the 3-tonners, the frames of which were pressed from ⅜" plate in the boiler shop.

The two No.3 wagons (Nos.107 and 108) were despatched in December, 1919, to the Great Northern & Great Central Joint Railway but were returned six months later. No.108 was sold almost at once to Boots Pure Drug Co.Ltd. in Nottingham but No.107 served for about nine months as the Works demonstrator during which period it was used by the sales and publicity manager, Geoffrey Marreco, on a series of demonstrations to prominent borough surveyors. Geoffrey, born in 1882, whom we encountered in Part 1 as secretary and reporter of the Geared Engine Committee, was a man of many parts. By training he was an engineer having served his time with Willans & Robinson of Rugby, noted as builders of high-speed steam engines much used in electricity generation and also as makers of steam turbines under the patents of Charles Parsons, and having served them subsequently as an area erection manager. He arrived on the Leiston scene, as the result of answering an advertisement, to serve as assistant to Stephen Garrett who was the director in charge of sales and, hence, of publicity. After Stephen's death he took over these managerial functions. Under the Garretts he did well but soon after the AGE was formed he was transferred to London where gradually he fell foul of the peculiar management practices of the group and eventually he left. Victor Garrett once commented to me that he (Victor) felt that Marreco had been shabbily treated by AGE, but despite that they kept in touch with each other and remained good friends until Marreco died in the 1970's.

These demonstrations by No.107, despite having secured a useful number of sales to commercial users during 1920, had failed to make any significant impression upon the municipal market. No.148, a 2½-tonner, had been completed in late Spring, 1921, and on May 23 of that year it was fitted temporarily with back-to-back upholstered seats to carry passengers at the Royal Show. It was also fitted with a larger driving sprocket to improve its running speed. In an endeavour to boost the municipal sales Geoffrey Marreco devised a publicity tour of some thirty miles in the hilly district of Yorkshire and Derbyshire along what is now the A625 from Sheffield to Bamford, taking in such land marks as the Toad's Mouth rock, two miles to the east of Hathersage. For this he took No.148 to Sheffield, where it was registered as WA4929, ready for its task in late October. On this occasion four teak garden seats provided the accommodation for his ten guests and, as a precaution, he provided for two cars to accompany the expedition, as well as arranging a photographer to go along. Unfortunately the day was dull and cold and most of the party were glad of the lunch and drinks he had laid on with Mrs. Butler, landlady of the Marquis of Granby Hotel at Sickleholme. By electric vehicle standards substantial sales resulted from this demonstration of the Garrett's ability to climb hills and the effectiveness of the brakes downhill. No.148 remained a demonstrator for about a year but was sold in October, 1922, to Jewson & Sons, the Norwich timber merchants, having first had the cab reduced in width to allow long timbers to be carried and having been fitted with a windscreen.

When AGE set up a London showroom in Aldwych, Marreco arranged for the 2½-tonner No.132, a standard non-tipper, to be completed as a bare chassis, without platform or cab, with a dummy battery supplied by Chloride, a wooden dummy motor made at Leiston, and wheels with painted wooden tyres instead of solid rubbers. These latter were put on only after it had reached the showroom, and the rubber tyred wheels on which it had travelled were sent home to Leiston. After some three years of exhibition No.132 returned to Leiston where it was given a Bull 9HP motor; improved brakes; a cab and bodywork; and the fresh number 219. Thus refurbished it went to Ilfracombe UDC on October 10, 1923.

During the period when the Station Works was being cleared of the war-time shell and aeroplane production lines electric vehicle production was somehow crammed into the already over-crowded Town Works, but with the changes that followed the creation of the AGE combine it was relocated at the Station Works. The somewhat grandiose and, in the event mostly unrealised, production intentions of the new combine have already been discussed in the preceding parts as has the upheaval in the drawing office as the long-smouldering distaste of Col. Garrett for H.K. Pratt, the then chief draughtsman, burst into flame resulting firstly in Pratt's sideways promotion to the Sales Office in Newcastle-upon-Tyne and shortly afterwards in his departure from the firm. Cuppleditch left at the end of March, 1920, though whether voluntarily or because he was nudged is not now known.

His successor was Alain J. Serve, a Frenchman by birth but resident for some years in Britain, who took up his duties as soon as Cuppleditch left, thus suggesting that the latter's departure must have been in amicable circumstances with long notice. His immediately preceding appointment had been with the Silvertown Works in London. Serve had long been gone by the time I knew Leiston but many people remembered him. Examples of his immaculate written English survive and he was recalled as having a complete command of the spoken language also but delivered with a pronounced Continental accent. Despite a chronically pessimistic disposition he had an enviable grasp of his subject and produced designs that were to earn Garrett electric vehicles a satisfied clientele in an extremely constricted market in which battery electric sales of all kinds were outnumbered by over one hundred to one by the internal combustion engined vehicles.

In 1919, spurred by the merger and probably sensing that the electric vehicle department was not in the 'ball-of-fire' category, the directors had commissioned a report to advise them on the merits of the contemporary Garrett designs relative to those of their competitors and on how marketing them might be improved. Doubtless for this they turned to F.E. Walker, their resident adviser on such matters, but Marreco and Plane also may have had a part in it. The report, dated December 23, 1919, is informative in many ways, not least in its tabulation of actual performance levels both by Garrett vehicles and by their competitors. It is too long to quote here in full so it has, therefore, been set out in Appendix 1. The report refers at some length to the importance of having specialist staff for selling electrics, but this was lost in the upheaval of the early AGE days when, for a spell, sales were concentrated at the London head office. The point was never wholly taken on board by higher management until the selling of trolley buses (see Chapter 4) finally forced the appointment of a salesman specifically for that purpose. It also led, by a process already described in Part 2, to Jack Simpson joining the sales staff, bringing with him the benefit of a sound engineering background and an acute intellect. Notwithstanding the question mark over the ability of the general run of Garrett salesmen to sell electric vehicles there were some successes, notably W.R.Montgomery, encountered in Part 2, who developed an enthusiasm for electrics that could lead him into overstating their capabilities. Having witnessed the erosion of Geoffrey Marreco's position under the AGE regime, Montgomery decided that his career would be more likely to advance in other spheres and accepted the post of manager of the Alton Battery Co.Ltd. in Hampshire which he held for many years.

To revert to the designs of the wagons it may be of interest to note that the first electric vehicle drawing list to appear in the register against Serve's initials was No.266 dated July 1, 1920, and headed 'Electric Vehicle Specification'. The last list produced by Cuppleditch was No.247, relating to the No.5 wagon, against which no actual date appears though it is sandwiched between a list dated June 11 and another from August 28, 1919. The wagons delivered during 1920, totalling twenty-seven in addition to Nos.103 and 104, must, therefore, have been to designs basically by Cuppleditch. These wagons were described by size numbers (i.e. No.3, No.4, or No.5) rather than by load capacity, but after the end of 1920 only four No.3's, viz. Nos.163, 179, 180, and 181, and no No.4 or No.5 wagons were sold, all others being marketed under carrying capacity, except for the light 'C' class wagons aimed at retail delivery and the 'E' class, all of which will be discussed shortly. Of the twenty-seven wagons under consideration, five were sold to local government bodies, the remainder being for trading companies or railways. It seems probable, therefore, that the change in the description of the wagons coincided with the arrival of Serve and the implementation of some of the amendments suggested in the 1919 report. For that matter, it also coincided with the removal of the electric vehicle assembly shop to the Station Works. Perhaps as a result of Geoffrey Marreco's demonstration and his persuasive skills, the overwhelming majority of subsequent vehicles were for local administrations.

In the euphoric 'sellers' market' atmosphere brought about by the temporary shortage of road vehicles immediately after the War and amidst the exaggerated optimism of the early days of AGE the decision was taken to build electrics for stock rather than against firm orders as was the case with most of the steam vehicle production. Unfortunately the rate of building never came anything near to what contemporary management would accept as 'mass-production' because, despite savage price cutting, it proved to be impossible to sell at a rapid rate. Hence the numerical sequence often failed to coincide with the date sequence, as will be seen from Appendix 4. Moreover, the picture was further complicated by the fact that exhibition or demonstration vehicles that had remained in stock for a long time were often renumbered and redated so as to dispel any feeling by the purchaser that his new wagon might in fact be part-used. Of the 353 numbers in the electric vehicle series eight (Nos. 119, 175, 215, 260, 288, 296, 305 and 334) seem never to have been carried, some because the order to which they were allocated was cancelled, and others simply by being passed over. The selling was done, in the main, by the in house selling system, and only a few home orders were supplied through trade intermediaries. Two (Nos.133 and 134) for E.C. Robson & Sons Ltd. of Sunderland were sold through Christy Brothers of Chelmsford, the electrical generation company that owned numbers of small local power stations including the one at Aldeburgh. Another, No.151, for the Fife Electric Power Co. went via Balfour Beatty & Co.Ltd. John Birch & Co., the London confirming house with whom the firm had dealt over the export of steam vehicles to the Far East, acted as agents for Calcutta Corporation in the purchase of Nos.145 and 148.

Despite the fact that the market for battery electrics was so limited it was soon to become hotly contested. As noted in Chapter 1 Electricars Ltd. began making Edison type vehicles in Birmingham in 1920, whilst Newton Brothers of Derby, old established as manufacturers of electrical equipment, entered the market about the same time, pursuing a most aggressive sales policy. The General Vehicle Co.Ltd. in Hay Mills, Birmingham, began building there in 1916 having previously imported electrics from its American parent company. Getting an order in the face of this competition usually meant savage price cutting. The ambition of AGE and of Col. Garrett himself to secure a major part of what market there was caused the selling department to embark upon an 'orders at any price' policy quoting prices that forced the competition into a state of alarm. In Chapter 1 reference was made to the introductory paragraphs of a memorandum from Col. Garrett to his fellow directors concerning a meeting he had had on July 7, 1921, with Monnot, Managing Director of Electricars Ltd., and also to an earlier but still recent meeting with him. Referring to this earlier meeting he noted:

On this occasion he evidently only wanted our A.G.E. Electric Stowmarket Motor which has given such excellent results and he evidently felt the competition - we therefore let the matter drop.

17

In the interval between the two meetings Monnot had evidently become alarmed at the Garrett course of conduct and was considering whether or not they might be able to take over the making of the Electricars chassis. What the Colonel's memorandum had to say of this was as follows:

At this last interview on Thursday I quickly saw it was Chassis he was after owing to the fierce competition in prices that we had set up, and the success we had lately obtained by the Sheffield, Hampstead, East Ham and other orders. He remarked we were evidently out to win, and God help our competitors! I told him this was so, and we were absolutely determined on this policy, and that nothing would stop us, telling him that Ransomes had even applied to us as to the feasibility of our supplying them a motor.

Monnot then went on to sound out the possibility of Electricars Ltd. joining the AGE combine:

He then asked me if I thought my Board (A.G.E.) would entertain the absorption of the Electricars Ltd. on the same terms as other Firms, they disposing of the Birmingham works and cutting their losses over the enterprise, perhaps retaining enough of the works as garage, charging station and repairs for the service of that neighbourhood. He also said that Eddison's [sic] Battery Company would be prepared to share expenses and use our service depots for their Battery business and upkeep arrangements. The same would apply to their premises in Seymour Street, where they not only deal with the Battery business but have a good business in repairs, charging, and upkeep contracts, which he said were very profitable. The same would also apply to any other instituted throughout the country. Also he said that Eddison's Accumulators Ltd., who are large shareholders in Electricars Ltd., would be prepared to grant a permanent beneficial arrangement in the price of the Eddison Transport Battery far below what the others could purchase them at.

I then told him I thought we really preferred the Knife [sic] Battery even to his as far as our experience went and from what I had heard of Ransomes. He denied this and spoke of various short-comings, and also said it would not stand up to its work anything like the Eddison, and that his was by far the most perfect of Alkaline Batteries.

My conclusions are that this offer is a great victory for the Garrett Electric Vehicle if we can only come to terms, and that it could be only too readily snapped up by our competitors should they have the opportunity.

Over 2,000 vehicles are to-day running with this Battery in this country. The agreement should be made for England and the Colonies. The Electricars Ltd. has only been running for some twelve months and has turned out some 250 cars. I take it that he has not obtained a satisfactory mechanical efficiency with this chassis and that their motors have given them trouble, and that it is in the best interests of the A.G.E. that either Mr. Monnot's absorption plan should be adopted, or some agreement reached with him for the manufacture of their chassis. I lean to the former, as they have a most efficient sales organization and are in touch for repairs and upkeep etc. of over 2,000 cars, besides having the call of Harrods (some 80 cars) and other large customers who are using Walker light cars with Eddison Batteries - by them they swear.

I have told Mr.Monnot that I would report to my Board this interview and see him further in the matter.

I may say that Mr. Monnot is a very difficult man, but I have always got on very well with him, and he said, if necessary, he would remain on Electricars' Board for a time but that at any time he would be at our disposal for advice and help.

It is a matter of history that this suggestion was not entertained. Electricars continued in business, underwritten by the vast resources of the American parent, and, in the end, it was Garretts who succumbed first.

This fazing of the opposition by Garretts in 1920/21 had, however, been achieved at a very high price, much to the concern of C. Gordon Melrose at the Works. Besides being a director Melrose was an accountant by training, and the economics of this sales drive jarred upon both of his disciplines. On November 19, 1921, he wrote to Victor Garrett at his private address in Hampstead, London, expressing his unease:

<u>Electric Vehicle Costs</u>

I have now prepared an up-to-date cost of the 2½-ton Chassis. On the assumption that 12½% has come off the wages, the cost is as follows:-

Material	£639. 13. 2d.
Labour	144. 16. 11d.
Tools and Charges at 125%	181. 1. 2d.
	965. 11. 3
Delivery	23. 7. 6
Starting up	5. 11. 0.
	£994. 9. 9.

I understand that the present list selling prices are as follows:-

	Home		Abroad
Gross List Price	£1133. 0. 0d.		£1133. 0. 0d.
Less 10%	113. 0. 0.	(15%)	170. 0. 0.
	1020. 0. 0.		963. 0. 0.
Less 2½%	25. 0. 0.		24. 0. 0.
	£ 995. 0. 0.		£ 939. 0. 0.

The cost includes an IMV.7 Battery, as a matter of fact, an IMV.8. is often supplied, and I believe is always supplied with a Tipper. (The difference in cost between the IMV.7. and 8. is £20, and I did not take this into account in the cost of the Tipping Gear shown to you yesterday.

You will realise how difficult it is for me to say that these prices should be reduced. Further you will notice that I have taken the tools and charges at 125%. I think I am safe in saying that our rate of overhead charges is, at the moment, between 250% to 300%. This you will realize from the following figures:-

Productive Wages at the moment, say, £700. per week - £35,000p.a.

Expenses Roughly

All unproductive labour which averages about 40% of productive	£14,000. p.a.
Interest, say	£12,000. p.a.
Total Sales Expenses. (Estimate for the future impossible, but if continued at A.G.E. rate)	£20,000. p.a.
Salaries	£24,000. p.a.
Total	£70,000. p.a.

You can understand that all our other expenses of establishment and depreciation come to a very considerable total.

This letter was one factor in bringing about the abandonment of the extravagant process of selling via group head office. It also earned Melrose the displeasure of the group chairman, Gwilym Rowland, and probably was one of the factors that soon caused Melrose to leave Garretts in order to join Shell - a spectacularly successful transition for him and a sad day for Garretts and AGE.

The personnel of the electric vehicle department at Leiston Works could not have known of this debate, and their immediate concern was the improvement of the vehicles themselves. On the whole, design policy on electric vehicles was decided, or at least discussed, at meetings of an electric vehicle committee which was convened from time to time under the chairmanship of Col. Garrett supported from the Board by his brother Alfred and Gordon Melrose. Other Works people usually present were W. Hall, the Works Manager (no relation to Walter Hall who helped to erect the first electric), Frank Walker, and A.J. Serve. H.C. Waters of AGE Electric Motors Ltd. was a co-opted member. The meeting of August 18, 1921, took a number of important decisions, probably the foremost of which was to instruct Serve to proceed with the preliminary design of a new 5-tonner, to be designated the 'G' type, and to prepare costings in conjunction with Hall for presentation to the next Board meeting on September 8. Another matter of concern considered at the same meeting was the excess weight of the bodies being designed for the electric vehicles by the Thresher Department, under Arthur Orange, and Serve was deputed to confer with Orange on how this might be reduced. One course suggested was that Serve himself should produce drawings for a light weight metal body to be used as standard. The question was important as it was related to the mileage per charge achieved by electrics and also to the simultaneous discussion as to whether the motors used should be wound for 60 or 80 volts. Perhaps against Serve's better judgement it was decided to use the 60 volt motor in 1½ and 2½-tonners, though the final reduction ratios were left open for further consideration.

Lastly the meeting discussed controllers. Those made by Vickers had superseded the Crompton type used in the first electric but still suffered from arcing. As Serve had pointed out, when cutting in or out traction currents such as they were using it was inevitable that arcing would take place, but by suitable design it was possible to cause this to occur in a switch rather than at the fingers. His new design of four speed controller giving effect to this suggestion was noted at the August 18 meeting as being virtually complete and it was resolved to use no more Vickers gear once the home produced article was ready.

Serve found himself at variance with the Works when the first of the new controllers was tried as it failed to live up to expectations in that arcing was not isolated to the magnetic blow-out switch as intended, but continued to occur at the fingers. The problem narrowed down principally to the controller drums not being absolutely interchangeable, so that when they were drilled for the contacts, the positioning of the latter varied in relation to the drum, some making good and others imperfect connection. These problems and various experiments with the blow-out switch (made at Stowmarket) were ironed out between Serve and Hall, though not without a few brisk exchanges in one of which Serve remarked 'The controller ..... came up to expectations only from the time when it was finally brought to correspond with the drawings. The brush gear generally may require more careful adjustment in the first instance.'

Once these transitory production problems had been overcome the controller gave good service though eventually it was replaced by a further revised version, again provided with eight speeds.

As far as motors were concerned, the first thirty-five or so vehicles had motors by Vickers but though these were satisfactory in many respects they had shortcomings, particularly in the brush gear and in the weight. Upon Serve's arrival at Leiston he set about producing a design of his own for a lighter motor which it was intended to build there but the joining of East Anglian Engineering to the AGE group caused motor building to be transferred to Stowmarket. How far the actual detail of Serve's motor was used at Stowmarket is now impossible to know. Apart from occasional differences of opinion, Serve and Waters respected each other and were good collaborators. Certainly the brush gear used was of Waters' devising and, moreover, it was such an improvement that it was fitted to some of the Vickers motors in stock at Leiston.

The first vehicle to leave the Works with a 'Bull' (or, as the memorandum book called it, a 'Stowmarket' motor) was No.139, sent off on August 25, 1921, though the first in numerical sequence to be so equipped was No.137, first destined for export but after cancellation of that order transferred to the London & South Western Railway to whom it was despatched on December 24, 1921. The use of Bull motors did not become invariable. It would be difficult to record with conviction which make of motor was used in any specific vehicle in the Autumn and Winter of 1921 as the Vickers motors in stock had to be used up, even if hybridised to some extent. That apart, the batch of chain driven 5-tonners (Nos.227-235 inclusive) for Sheffield Corporation in 1923-24 were all equipped with GEC (Schenectady) motors of 11HP type GE1087, though the motor on the tipping gear in each case was by Bull. No.236, the solitary worm driven GT for Sheffield had, by contrast, a BTH motor. Probably customer preference accounted for this variation.

These developments lived in the shadow, so far as Melrose was concerned, of the apprehension he felt about the sales drive. This is brought out in a memorandum which he directed to Victor Garrett through the official channels at London Office emphasising the capital tied up in electric vehicle stocks, and in the demonstrators and exhibition vehicles. This was dated November 30, 1921.

Electric Vehicle Demonstrations

I have been looking into the matter of stock Vehicles at demonstrations etc., and think the position is so serious that we should turn our faces against further requests for demonstrations until some of this stock is cleared.

The following is a list of the Vehicles which are I think out on demonstration, or returned to the Works from demonstration or Shows:-

Size	No.	
No.4	132	London Showroom
4	136	Demonstrating in Dundee - since sent to Glasgow
5	146	London & North Western Railway demonstration - now at Leiston
4	148	Demonstrating in Sheffield
5	160	Demonstrating in Colchester
5	123	Demonstrating in Dublin
5	174	Demonstrating in Bristol
3	153	Demonstrating in South America

Vehicles returned ex Shows

No.5	172	ex Brewers Exhibition
4	173	ex Roads & Transport Exhibition (to be demonstrated at Finsbury next week).

This is an enormous amount of stock to be carrying apart from the stock which we have at Leiston. Most important of all is the question of Batteries. Each of these Vehicles, except the first (which has a dummy battery), has a Battery which is now secondhand. The Chloride Company's guarantees date from one month after delivery from their Works, so that although some of these Batteries may not have been used very much, they are depreciating in the Vehicles and can only be disposed of at a big sacrifice.

Arising out of this question, I would like to make it a rule that when we sell a Vehicle the Battery should be sent direct from the makers. Before making this a definite decision however, perhaps you should ask the opinion of the various E.V. salesmen. I have already written Chloride Company asking them if they will be willing to guarantee that their Inspectors will receive the Batteries and have them fully formed and charged at the Customers places of business before the latter attempt to use the Vehicles for service. - I think they will agree to this.- This procedure in any case would save us carriage on the battery, acid etc., and man's time charging up the batteries here for the first time.

We must have at least £3,000 worth of Batteries in stock depreciating daily, and I wish to make a big effort to get this reduced.

The first entirely new design completed after Serve's arrival at Leiston was the 'C'-class. Like the No.3 wagon and its revamped derivatives this was intended for a 1½ ton payload but with a different category of user in mind, being aimed at the retail tradesman. The 'C' was originally designed with a two motor drive, the motors being produced specially for the purpose by AGE Electric Motors. When the first 'C' was tested at the end of October, 1921, the results were found to be very disappointing. Serve arranged a comparison with results obtained earlier from two of the old type No.3 1½-tonners, the identity of which is not known. The first (A) had a Vickers motor and an IMV7 battery; the second (B) had a Stowmarket motor wound for 60 volts and an IMV9 battery, while the 'C' class vehicle had an IMV9 battery. The table of these results is set out below:

Vehicle	AmpereHours per mile	A.H. per ton mile	Average Speed	Average speed on level	Total Weight as run	Approx. Mileage per charge
A	6.48	1.17	10.7	12	5. 10. 1	26
B	7.37	1.248	13.5	14.5	5. 18. 0	40
C	7.57	1.48	12.2	11.1	5. 2. 1	31

Even the older wagon with the Vickers motor outperformed the new 'C' except in the matter of speed, and the latter's superiority in this respect depended on its better ability to coast because it was shaft driven whereas the older vehicle had chain drive. The lower distance per charge (26 miles) with this wagon was, of course, the consequence of its having a much smaller battery. The other wagon (B in the table) equipped with the Bull motor eclipsed the 'C's performance still further. After some debate (or argument perhaps) about why this should have been the case the decision was made to redesign the 'C' with a single motor. This design, even as revised, was the only part of the electric vehicle venture that could fairly be described as a total failure. One 'C' class chassis was sold, No.188, which went to Robert Mitchell & Sons Ltd. in Glasgow, for J. & B. Stevenson, the celebrated Glasgow bakers, who had a van body built upon it. A second vehicle, No.212, built as a demonstrator, officially never found a purchaser and was broken up in April, 1928. What actually took place was that chassis No.188, having proved unsatisfactory to the purchasers for reasons now unknown, was returned to Robert Mitchell & Sons and in its stead chassis No.212 was sent from Leiston. The J. & B. Stevenson body was transferred to No.212 which then assumed the identity of No.188. The unsatisfactory chassis was sent back to Leiston and was eventually dismantled for scrap. Somewhat later two further examples of a slightly modified design, the 'C2' were built. No.220 (July 31, 1924) was sold to the Borough of Grimsby whilst No.221, which had been completed on March 13, 1925, as a 1½-tonner for demonstration to J.Lyons & Co. Ltd. and altered in April to a 2-tonner (hence the 'C2') by amending the springs and substituting a worm gear with a lower reduction factor, was sold finally on September 28, 1925, to Clark & Fauset, the Garrett agents in Brisbane. Another C2, No.263 (October 29, 1925), had kerbside control which was removed prior to sale on January 6, 1928, to the Automobile Electric Supply Co. (Cape) Ltd. in Cape Town. The final 'C', No.390, was despatched on July 20, 1928, to the same firm, and was still held there for Garretts in 1931.

The production version of the 'C' marked a total departure from the No.3 and its 1½ ton successor, particularly in its emphasis upon lightness. The chassis was pressed out of high tensile steel, assembled with bolts. Similarly the wheels were high tensile pressed steel discs. A single 9 HP Bull motor was placed longitudinally well forward in the chassis driving through a cardan shaft with Hardy disc couplings onto a Timken Detroit rear axle by way of David Brown worm gear. The sheet steel axle casing was pressed in two parts and welded together. A foot operated controller gave eight forward speeds and seven in reverse. The front axle bed, steering pivots, and stubs were of nickel steel. Roller bearings were fitted to both front and rear wheels. The vehicle was altogether lighter - the chassis weighing 35 cwt. compared with 50 cwt. in the previous 1½ tonner - and much easier to steer. Although also offered on pneumatics at an extra price the examples built all ran on solid tyres, single all round - 110 x 771mm front and 120 x 771mm rear. The standard battery offered was a Kathanode lead acid type weighing 25 cwt. compared with 18 cwt. in its predecessors, but for this it offered 15 m.p.h. loaded on a good level road and a mileage of 40 to 45 per charge. The snag of this much improved vehicle, of course, was the price. The chassis on solids was offered at £490, plus £230 for the standard battery. If the alternative of an Edison A8 (nickel alkaline) battery was specified the battery cost leapt to £692 !

Probably a more interesting, and certainly commercially more successful, product of this revision and updating of the vehicles was the 'G', particularly the 'GT' tipping version, the drawing list for which was completed on March 16, 1923. Much of the work on this was done by W.H. (Bill) Deane who had recently joined Serve in the electric vehicle section and was later to be involved in the trolley bus project, recounted in Chapter 4. The 'GT', like the much lighter 'C', was shaft driven to an overhead worm drive rear axle and was aimed primarily at refuse collection where the earlier models also had had their most satisfactory sales. The 'G' class represented a far more modern image than the earlier 2½ and 3½-tonners. The 11HP motor was turned through 90° so as to suit the cardan shaft drive, with Hardy fabric joints, which drove the live rear axle via the overhead worm. The front axle had a Kirkstall beam and Lavine (Model M25) steering. The wheels were high tensile steel discs with solid rubber tyres. The batteries were carried in pannier boxes alongside the chassis, the tops doubling as running boards, and supplementary battery space was provided under a bonnet, finished with a cast aluminium alloy false 'radiator'. Much better cabs were provided, as will be seen from the illustration, and the lorry built for Manchester Corporation had drop glass in the cab doors. Serve's 'run back and tip' gear operated by a horizontal drive rod and gears driven by a small motor beneath the driving seat, used on tippers since he had designed it in the Autumn of 1921, was abandoned in favour of Edwards' oildraulic gear with its own ram pump and AGE motor. Without doubt the 'G' controls came much more into line with conventional lorry practice, with the foot operated controller replacing the accelerator of a petrol engined lorry. In both appearance and characteristics they did go some way towards re-impressing the idea of electric vehicles upon the collective municipal mind, but the bother and expense of the batteries needing renewal every two to three years taken in conjunction with the high initial cost told against them.

Later in 1923 the theme was further developed into the 'GTS' articulated 6-wheeler. Here Garretts had hit upon an arrangement that anticipated the much later Scammell Electricar articulated refuse vehicles but once more the idea was too far in advance of its time to be a commercial success. One example was built, No.242 delivered on July 16, 1924, to the City of Norwich. The first 'GT' to be delivered was No.236 for Sheffield Corporation, despatched on February 12, 1924, followed by a batch of five (Nos.237 to 241) delivered to Birmingham Corporation in February and March, 1924. The same customer had a further twelve (Nos.248-259 inclusive) between May and July, 1925, and four more (Nos.269-272) about a year later, from which it would seem to be fair to deduce that they were very pleased with their purchases. What is baffling is that when one municipal client found the 'GT' obviously satisfactory no other customers came forward for similar refuse collection vehicles. Indeed only one further example of the 'GT' was sold - No.311 sent to Manchester Corporation Electricity Department as a lorry in early October, 1926. Two of the basic 'G' type went to commercial purchasers. These were No.266, despatched to Boots Pure Drug Co.Ltd. in Nottingham on March 3, 1926, and No.267 to Hovis Ltd. of Battersea, London, on January 14, 1927. Hovis ordered their wagon to be sent in grey primer only for their coach painters to carry out the finished paintwork. As narrated in Part 2 concerning their undertype steam wagons, even in the best of circumstances Hovis were demanding clients. By July 22, 1927, the wagon was brought back to Leiston to deal with the owner's complaints. Cyril Plane, one of Maurice Plane's sons, took it, loaded with 6 tons, twice round the standard test circuit from Leiston to Aldeburgh with F.Newton driving. They found that the controller was in poor condition and arcing badly whilst the brakes were insufficient to hold the wagon on the 1 in 7½ gradient of Cullens Hill, Aldeburgh. On the second circuit the wagon refused altogether to climb this hill. The defects were rectified and the wagon returned to Hovis. It came back a second time early in October, after further complaints about shortcomings in its performance. Suspecting that the motor might be at fault the Works swapped it for the one intended for a Glasgow vehicle. The same pair took it out on test on October 5, during which it touched 25 m.p.h. entering Aldeburgh down Warren Hill. As Cyril Plane remarked drily 'This proves the bearings are quite free.' Nevertheless it still refused to take its 6 ton load up Cullens Hill. Various adjustments of the brushes in relation to the commutator were tried, and eventually it was decided that the optimum result had been obtained though the vehicle was never coaxed up Cullens Hill with a load. On October 19 it was tested satisfactorily in the presence of Mr. Heigh, the engineer/surveyor of the British Engine & Boiler Insurance Co., on behalf of Hovis, and on his recommendation it was accepted by Hovis.

These two 'G' types were followed in the numerical sequence by a solitary 3½ tonner, No.268, classified as 'E' type, again shaft driven. Although this was begun on January 7, 1926, no buyer was found and the nearly completed vehicle, which began life as a short wheelbase tipper, remained in hand throughout 1926 and 1927. Finally, in response to an order via the agency of the Automobile Electric Supply Co. (Cape) Ltd., who had had a 'C' type two months earlier, it was exported to South Africa. This involved removing the tipping gear and extending the chassis, the Works plate being re-stamped '1928', before the wagon left the Works on March 2. Although it was fitted to receive a Chloride battery, this was shipped direct by the battery manufacturers. Two worm driven 3½ ton end-tippers, (Works Nos.264 and 265) were sold on February 24 and March 4, 1926, to the Borough of Ipswich and the City of Nottingham respectively. One further 3½ ton vehicle, probably but not certainly of the same design as these, was assembled in the late Summer of 1928, supposedly as a demonstrator. This was on the Works until July 23, 1930, when it was renumbered 433 and sold to St.Albans.

For a while the firm apparently acquiesced in the face of the collapse of demand for battery electrics but in 1928, in the perennial search for ways of reviving the flagging output, the possibility of reviving it

Figs. 13 (above) and 14 (below). No.147 (June, 1921) was a 3½-tonner incorporating Serve's revisions. It had been dragged out unpainted and, indeed, unfinished (see the untrimmed canvas at the edge of the cab roof) to be photographed in Carr Avenue, Leiston. The wagon was for the Calcutta Corporation. The 10 cwt crane was by the Chatteris Engineering Co.

Fig.15. In 1920/21 Sheffield Corporation became the satisfied owners of a fleet of 2½-ton Garrett electrics, the first of which was No.118 (sixth from left). This was a No. 4 to Cuppleditch's original design, but the remainder were to Serve's updated design using his patent controller. The original Vickers controller on No.118 was replaced by the new pattern in March, 1923.

Fig.16. Because Sheffield were so happy with their purchases, in October, 1921, Geoffrey Marreco, of Garretts, organised a demonstration of what a 2½-tonner could do in the hilly terrain west of Sheffield, using No.148, already shown at the Royal Show that year - note the brass hub caps. To it he invited a select band of municipal engineers. Teak seats provided the seating, with two cars for those who valued comfort more. The route, using current classification, ran west along the A625 to Bamford, north up the A6013 to Ladybower Reservoir, and home to Sheffield on the A57.

Fig.17. The route gave plenty of opportunity to demonstrate hill climbing ability.

Fig.18. *A pause at the Toad's Mouth. Marreco is the figure*
at the left of the group seated below the rock.

Fig.19. *The day was dull and chill enough to make the lunch and drinks laid on*
at Mrs. Butler's Marquis of Granby Hotel, *Sickleholme, very acceptable.*

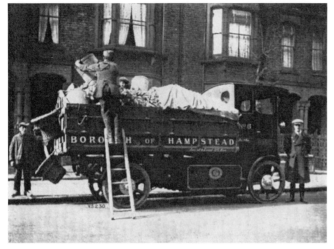

Fig.20. No.173, a 3½-tonner, began life in Autumn, 1921, as a demonstrator, going, inter alia, *to the Roads & Transport Exhibition. In May, 1922, Hampstead Borough Council bought it as a dustcart, numbering it 6 in their fleet. The picture illustrates the problems of loading the old high-sided type (compare the GTZ design in Fig.2).*

Fig.21. They already had No.162 (fleet No.5) on the right in this picture, with the slightly earlier design of cab. Winter, the Hampstead Surveyor, would not have cab doors on the Council's vehicles.

Fig.22. The slightly later quartet (222 to 225) supplied in October and November, 1923, to Southend Borough Council had the Collins kerbside control and by having windscreens and cab doors showed a more benevolent employer.

Fig.23. An artist's impression of the 1-ton 'B' type, planned but never built. Had it been produced it would have been aimed at retail delivery, in which, after about 1935, most electrics were used.

came into boardroom discussion again. Arthur Bennett, one of the AGE appointed directors, wrote to Victor Garrett, who by then was Managing Director of the Eddison Steam Rolling Co. Ltd. in Dorchester, on July 10, 1928:

> The question of our going again actively into the Battery Vehicle market is again being raised. What we need is some data as to the demand there still is for this type of Vehicle. I know you were closely in touch with all that was being done, owing to your connection with the E.V.M.A.
>
> I shall be very grateful if you can give me any information you have as to - say, the number of orders taken by the various makers in this country in the past twelve months for Electric Battery Vehicles, with any data you may have as to the type of Vehicle, i.e. whether of the light 1-tonner type or of the heavier kinds.
>
> Our last review about eighteen months ago left us with the impression that the demand was dwindling very seriously. Has there been any change of which you are aware?

Victor wrote back suggesting he sent for the Ministry of Transport's newly instituted quarterly digests of vehicles registered for the first time. When he received them. Bennett can have gained little comfort from what he read. In the five quarters ending in May, 1928, only 97 battery electrics had been newly registered! In thanking Victor Garrett for his letter he commented:

> Personally, unless and until battery weights are reduced enormously below those at present prevailing, I find it hard to visualise any real vogue for electric vehicles.

Time has proved this opinion to have been absolutely correct.

In the production policy discussions of August, 1921, it was made clear that had the initial two motor version of the 'C' class been successful the intention was to replace the existing 2½-tonner with a new lighter weight version to be called the 'D', in much the same way that the 'E' superseded the old 3½-tonner. This never reached production. It had further been the intention to increase the range by building, for the first time, a light van in the 10/15 cwt class to be designated the 'B'. This was intended to have a single 80 volt motor drawing its current from an IMV7 battery, which would have given it a laden weight of some 60 cwt and the legal and practical opportunity to reach 20 m.p.h. No serious attempt was made to implement this proposal, yet the subsequent history of battery electrics as a class demonstrated that in the end vehicles of this weight, or less, exceeded all other battery electrics by odds of several hundred to one. To cite an example, Victor Electrics Ltd. of Burscough Bridge, Lancashire, founded their business which endured from 1927 to 1961 almost entirely upon products designed to carry less than 30 cwt. Abandoning the 'B' class must be considered a serious policy error.

A second product that was offered but never constructed was the Garrett electric tractor. E.A. Shadrack, the East London coal merchant, used Garrett overtype wagons and sometime in October, 1921, Victor Garrett and Teddy Ballam called on him to sound out the possibilities of further sales. The three men were old acquaintances and the conversation turned to possible replacements for the horse. Despite his two visitors lauding the capabilities of the battery electric lorry Shadrack asked instead what the possibilities were of producing an electric tractor capable of hauling about 2 tons on coal merchants' existing trolleys. Quite apart from his own needs, he assured his visitors, there would be a big demand from the trade as a whole for a power unit that could be transferred from trolley to trolley just as a horse was unharnessed from one and re-harnessed to another. Shadrack went so far as to say that if a suitable tractor could be produced he would give them an initial order for six. A little later Victor discussed these observations with Tyne Main who, at that time, also had a large stake in the London coal distribution business, and they confirmed what Shadrack had said. On the strength of these remarks Victor Garrett requested the Works to see what proposals could be made to these interested parties.

Victor Garrett's memorandum to the Works from the London Office was handed to Serve. It was dated October 21 and yet by November 8 Serve had not only roughed out a sketch design and an outline specification but had also, in conjunction with the costing office, produced a provisional price of £900 plus the cost of an IMV8 battery (at that time of the order of £300). Despite the fact that the price put off Shadrack, Tyne Main, and other London coal merchants, the tractor details plus an artist's impression were put into Catalogue No.604 though no sales resulted. The catalogue picture shows a tractor with a live rear axle but Serve's original advance specification proposed a shaft drive to a countershaft and thence a final drive by twin Hans Renold roller chains.

Nearly all of the electric refuse collectors that were sold went as replacements for horse drawn vehicles. A self-propelling dust cart provided a number of advantages over its equine-hauled predecessors but it had one serious shortcoming, namely that whereas most of the horses used were as tame as cats and would amble up a street unattended in response to a whistle thus freeing the driver to help with the bins, when an electric or a motor was substituted, the driver needed to be either in his seat the whole time or to be constantly climbing up and down. In 1921, a German electric refuse collection vehicle appeared equipped with a secondary set of controls that enabled it to be moved at low speed by a person walking alongside. The literature for this was first seen by W.R. Montgomery whose active mind saw in the innovation a means of Garretts securing a further share of the fast waning market in municipal refuse collection vehicles. The idea had already been put to Cuppleditch before he left, and he had dismissed it as impractical and dangerous. Serve, in his turn, produced a much more reasoned and less dismissive response in a letter to Gordon Melrose, dated November 8, 1921:

<u>Auxiliary Control</u>

I have given some thought to this question since Mr. Montgomery mentioned it to me, and I have come to the conclusion that it is not so simple as it sounds - It can be done - It will be complicated. And Mr. Montgomery loses sight of the fact that although he happens to have met with a system of refuse collection which expects the driver to load up, I believe the majority of systems do not work on that principle - It is all a question of methods of loading - in East Ham, or Sheffield for instance, the suggested auxiliary control would have no special advantages.

Perhaps the opinion of other Salesmen could be taken before any decision was arrived at. Hilly districts would also render this control dangerous. It must be realized that it involves three distinct problems:- (a) Steering - A small steering angle (see letter) assumes that all streets are straight. (b) A low speed sufficient on the level will not be so on up grades - this means practically a second controller. (c) Brake gear - This must be very powerful, as a man walking alongside cannot exert all his power in the same way as when he is sitting in the seat.

The suggestion, though still pressed by Montgomery and possibly also by Jack Simpson, was not approved wholeheartedly by Frank Walker, on whom the directors relied a good deal for sober advice on such matters, and it remained on the table well into 1922 when customer pressure forced action upon the firm, more or less against its will. A system of control devised by Mr. A.E. Collins, the City Engineer of Norwich, was put before the directors in Autumn, 1922, with the suggestion that it might be put into working drawing form in the Leiston Drawing Office. The drawing list (No.295) is actually dated November 15. Seventeen refuse vehicles are known to have been equipped with it - No.174 (a 3½-tonner) and a pair of 2½-tonners, Nos.186 and 187, for Norwich; No.213, which went the same year to St.Albans; No.214 for Rugby UDC; Nos.222-225 inclusive which were supplied to Southend-on-Sea; the Norwich 6-wheeler (No.242) plus Nos.289 - 295 inclusive, also for Norwich. There may well have been others. When the kerbside mechanism was brought into use a throw-over switch had to be operated to transfer control from the main eight speed controller to an auxiliary controller giving only four speeds with a maximum of 4m.p.h. The lever of the auxiliary projected from the panel below the driver's side window. It was spring-loaded and when the weight of the driver's hand was taken off, it returned to the neutral position. The auxiliary brake lever protruded just below the driver's door, working in a horizontal quadrant via the foot brake gear, and was provided with a locking clip which, it was hoped, would discourage malicious release of the brake when the driver was away from the vehicle. The operation of the auxiliary steering is better understood by reference to the drawing and captions (Figs.24, 25, and 26). It should be added that the same steering wheel, which was removable and attachable by a quick release mechanism, was used for driving from both the main and the auxiliary positions.

A further problem associated with the change from horse-drawn to electric-powered dust carts was that the height above kerb level of the loading apertures necessitated the use of loading ladders, which in turn slowed down the operation and contributed to fatigue in the binmen. Whilst the height of the body sides above the floor level was fixed by capacity requirements, the height of the loading rail above the kerb, on the other hand, resulted from the chassis height of the vehicle, dictated by the size of the battery box under the chassis. Petrol vehicles did not need a battery box and began to appear in designs with a much reduced line for bin-tipping. The most innovative and threatening of these rival designs was the *SD* low wheeled freighter designed by Harry Shelvoke and James Drewry which appeared in 1922 and appealed at once to local authorities. Within three years of the appearance of the *SD* the old high loading designs of dust cart had notice to quit. An appreciable improvement was achieved in the 'GT' vehicles when the Edwards' 'oildraulic' tipping gear was used in place of the run back and tip gear. This enabled wheel arches to be used over the rear wheels and the body to be set lower on the chassis. To some extent this brought the 'GT's more into line with petrol engined vehicles, but not, it seems, enough to turn the tide in favour of electrics. That is not to say, of course, that those already in service were withdrawn at once, nor that sales ceased totally, but in Garretts' case the market in even their 'GT' design came to an end in 1926. In 1925, just as trolley buses came into production - the subject of the next chapter - plugging the gap left by the diminished sales of the first generation of battery electrics, the firm made an audacious and successful bid for the supply to Glasgow Corporation of a completely re-thought battery electric design, incorporating a low loading line that finally disposed of the most serious bug-bear of the earlier models. How this came about is narrated in Chapter 5.

Figs.24 (right), 25 (lower left) and 26 (lower right) illustrate the general arrangement of the Collins-Garrett system of kerbside controls. The spring-loaded handle of the auxiliary controller (which gave 4m.p.h. maximum speed) returned to neutral when the driver's hand was taken off - a form of 'dead man's handle'. The trigger of the auxiliary brake lever could be locked by 'a simple unobtrusive clip'. The same steering wheel fitted on squares on the main and auxiliary columns, being secured by a quick release lever, turning which locked it on or eased it off. The working of the box which connected the two systems is explained by its makers thus:

Through the steering gear in its auxiliary position the shaft 'A' can be rotated. This through screw gear forms the vertical shaft 'B'. To the bottom of the latter is castellated a spur wheel 'C' in mesh with a smaller wheel 'C²' at the bottom of the main steering column and as both these and the screw gears are the same size the steering column 'D' is turned exactly the same amount as the auxiliary steering shaft 'A'. Thus through the thread and nut 'E' and the lever (not shown) the shaft and drag link 'F' which actuates the steering of the front wheels is moved.

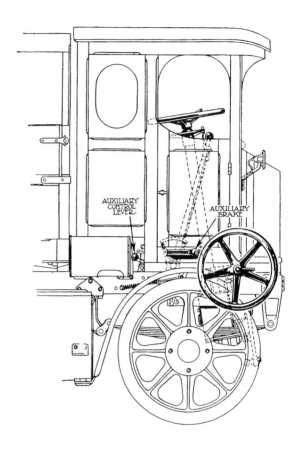

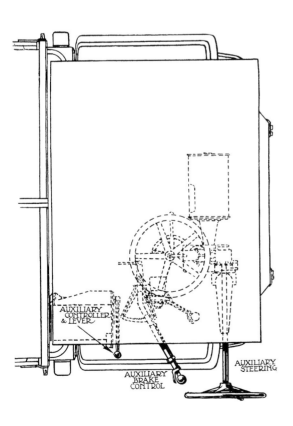

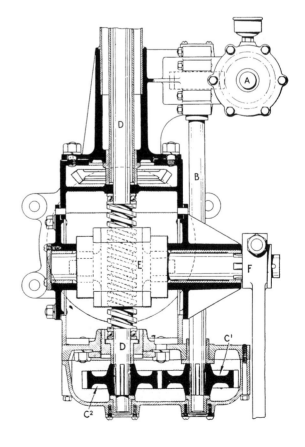

Fig.27. The 'C' type, a redesigned and lighter 30 cwt vehicle ought to have been very successful but failed to capture sales. This is No.188 for J. & B. Stevenson, the Glasgow bakers. The hexagonal device on the front hub is a step meant to help the driver or mate to get in and out more easily at the frequent stops required for town deliveries.

Fig.28. No.220 was the slightly larger C2 version of the 'C' class, intended for a 2 ton load. Originally ordered for New Zealand it was sold in July, 1924, to the Borough of Grimsby.

Fig.29. A drawing of the electric tractor intended for hauling the traditional London coal trolley. A promising enquiry from E. & A. Shadrack and interest by Tyne Main and other London coal merchants came to nothing because of the high estimated price of the tractor.

Fig.30. Morgans Brewery Co. of Norwich were owners of No.106, the third Garrett electric to be delivered (October 23, 1919). It was a platform lorry with chock rails, intended for barrelled beer.

Fig.31. By contrast No.144 for Mann Crossman & Paulin had the lattice sided body with a chain across the rear, which was much favoured by London brewers.

Fig.32. Nuttall & Co. Ltd. of Lion Brewery, Blackburn, had No.163 in July, 1921. It was a 2½-tonner for use in their mineral water business.

Fig.33. The first No.4 wagon delivered to a customer was No.105 which went to the Standard Wire Co. of Sowerby Bridge on September 20, 1919, but came back for amendments the next year when this picture was taken. The body and cab, not by Garretts, were very heavy. The design of apron was used on the first few wagons only. After that the pattern shown in Fig.32. was used, being cheaper to make. The oval brass plate, like that on steam engines, on the front of the chassis was soon to be replaced by the AGE pattern.

Fig.34. No.128, one of the trio of No.3 wagons (127, 128 and 129) sold to the Savoy Hotel Ltd., London, for transporting linen to and from its laundry.

Fig.35. (right) shows how the bodies of the Savoy Hotel vans were built using a form of stressed skin construction - 5 ply board on a framework of light ash sticks, stiffened by perforated metal lattices horizontally and diagonally. This was one of the lightest van bodies ever designed at Leiston.

Fig.36. (below), Another good looking van (but much heavier!), also a No.3, was No.154 for W. & R. Jacob, the Liverpool biscuit makers. The roof rack was for empty tins, returned for re-use, which were secured in the rack by a coarse net.

Fig. 37. The ten Garretts owned by Birmingham Corporation in 1924, five 3½-tonners and five newly delivered GT's. Another 12 GT's were soon to follow.

Fig.38. Twenty 3½-tonners in the fleet of Hackney Borough Council posed at the rear of the Council's Electricity Works, where the refuse was burned.

Chapter 3

Owners and Users

Among the battery electrics there was nothing like the rich diversity of types of owner and operator that occurred, for example, with the overtype steam wagons. Statutory undertakings and local authorities formed the bulk of the users, among whose vehicles there were some interesting and unusual types of bodies, but ordinary trade claimed a far from negligible minority, which, in its turn, embraced examples of bodywork that were by no means commonplace.

It is easy to picture the kind of factors that might have induced a large local council to look favourably upon an electric lorry. Many owned municipal electricity generating stations, some of which were fired on the refuse that the vehicles were destined to collect. The Metropolitan Borough of Hackney was one of the customers whose refuse collectors delivered their contents to a destructor plant. Garretts supplied only the chassis and cabs, the body being supplied by Ransomes & Rapier and consisting of a set of cradling to carry two demountable refuse tubs - which today would probably have been described as skips. The object of the design was twofold; to reduce the time lost by each wagon between the last pick-up of one trip and the first of the succeeding run; and to make handling of the collected refuse easier at the destructor. Since it was not feasible to increase the travelling speed, the tubs represented a serious and, I believe, within limits, successful attempt to save time at the discharge point. By having a surplus of tubs over carrying vehicles it was possible to demount two full tubs by means of an overhead hoist and to substitute two empties within two or three minutes. The loaded tubs were transported by the overhead carrier to one of the series of furnace firing points where the contents were discharged as required without double handling onto the firing floor to be fed into the fires by furnacemen. These individuals were saddled with probably the most revolting task in the whole process, exposed to the stench, dust and body vermin contained in the refuse. Virtually their only consolation, apart from having a job when many did not, was the occasional finding of a coin or some minor valuable. When the Glasgow GTZ fleet was put in hand (as described in Chapter 5) one of the major advances made was the mechanical firing of the destructor furnaces in which the refuse was burned.

Altogether Hackney had twenty-four Garrett 4/5 ton battery electrics, and of these all but one were used as refuse collectors. The sole exception was the first, No.185, which was an end tipper for use by the Electricity Department. Delivery of this had been promised for the first week of November, 1922, but in fact it was not despatched until January 8, 1923. Besides its more prosaic and routine work for the department No.185 had its prima donna moments when it took to the streets for carnivals and processions bedecked with a demountable roofed exhibition kiosk. Its most distinguished appearance in this guise was the occasion when it represented the British Electrical Industry in the 1923 Lord Mayor's Show in the City of London. A two part tableau showed a mediaeval citizen cooking with a cauldron supported on a tripod over a simulated twig fire at the cab end of the body whilst at the opposite end a modern housewife was shown preparing a meal in a kitchen replete with every available electrical aid. Besides the wagons they had new, Hackney Borough Council bought a further Garrett second-hand. This was No.161, a 2½-tonner originally supplied to Canterbury Borough Council in June, 1921, as a dual purpose vehicle in which an end tipping body was interchangeable with a 500 gallon Eagle street watering tank. It was already over nine years old when Hackney bought it in August, 1930.Three other London boroughs ran Garretts. Stepney had No.107, one of those built in the Summer of 1919 for the Great Northern, Great Central & Great Eastern Railways which were returned the next year. No.107 served for a while as a London demonstrator but, probably because of Melrose's misgivings concerning the capital tied up in demonstrators, was updated, overhauled and sold to Stepney in March, 1921. St.Pancras ordered two 3½-ton end tippers (Nos.182 and 183) in September, 1922, for use as dust-carts. These had long lives - spares were still being supplied for them as late as May, 1937. Hampstead had five (Nos.162, 173, 209, 210, and 211), the first in June, 1921. Most borough engineers had some special requirements of their own, and Oliver Winter at Hampstead insisted that there should be no side doors on the cab of No.162. The second Hampstead vehicle, No.173 of May, 1922, had the distinction of being the first to be fitted with Serve's new design of eight speed controller. To some extent it may have been a guinea pig for Serve's experiments as it was begun in August, 1921, and was thus over seven months in the making. No.209 came somewhat into the same category having been built originally in August and September, 1921, as No.172, a 3½-tonner but not delivered to Hampstead until mid-June, 1923, by which time it had

Fig.39. (right) Rear end of a City of Norwich 2½-tonner fitted with the Collins/Garrett kerbside control.

Fig.40. (below) Hackney Borough Council bought a fleet of twenty 4/5 tonners (Nos.189-208 inclusive) delivered between May and August, 1923. The bodies were cradles with cleats to hold a pair of skips (by Ransomes, Sims & Jefferies). This shows No.190 on its round with the ubiquitous and tiring ladder in position.

Fig.41. (bottom) No.198 loaded, being weighed in at the destructor while the driver and two fillers (binmen) stand on the right. The driver took his turn at filling which, as the wagons did not have kerbside controls, involved leaping in and out of the cab. About 180 tons of refuse were collected on an average day. This arrived at the plant during a period of about six hours and represented two round trips by each wagon per day.

Fig.42. Here wagon No.190 is seen under the overhead transporter which lifted the skips by the trunnions each side of them and took them to the firing floor. The furnace front can be seen below the skip and above the chassis. The sett road on which the wagon is standing was elevated, and had curved entrance and exit ramps.

Fig.43. No.208, the newest of the fleet, having emptied skips placed upon it. Getting this right required good co-ordination between the drivers of the crane and the wagon. When going well it could be very quick. Once the skips were in position and cleated the wagons descended the outgoing slope to be reweighed.

Fig.44. *Wagons emerging from the plant and on their way back to the weighbridge.*

Fig.45. No.202 about to be weighed (once the crew had stepped off the weighbridge). The baskets, shovels, and loading ladders would then be put back on ready for the next trip.

Fig.46. A little before the dustcarts were delivered the Hackney Council had No.185 for use by the Electricity Department. It acquired an alter ego *as the star of the Council's fleet, appearing in various carnivals and as the representative of the British Electrical Industry in the 1923 Lord Mayor's Show in the City of London.*

been metamorphosed into a 2½-tonner. However, the other two wagons delivered at the same time - 210 and 211 - were both entirely new. Out of deference to the Hampstead hills they all had 9HP motors.

Outside London, the largest Garrett fleet in England was that owned by the City of Birmingham, numbering twenty-six in all. Beginning in 1921 with two 3½-tonners (Nos.164 and 165), followed the next year by a further trio (Nos.179, 180 and 181), the Council took up with enthusiasm the new 5-ton GT design in 1924. By all accounts these did very well. In 1935 when the oldest was eleven years old a start was made in converting them to run on pneumatics. The necessary work was covered by specification (drawing list) No.815. This conversion system, like those designed for undertype steam wagons and for the Glasgow GTZ's, was the work of Leslie Farrow who was looked upon in the Leiston Drawing Office as the expert in the matter. He also devised the conversion of the even older No.112, despatched March 3, 1920, for the East Anglian Farmers Co-operative Association in Ipswich. Leiston Works supplied the parts, although the work of fitting them to the wagon was undertaken by its owners.

Though sales to local authorities for use as dust-carts dominated the latter part of the battery electric production, in its opening phase the reverse was the case. It is true the first wagon (No.102) to be built after the War went to Blackpool Corporation, but it was for use by the Corporation Electricity Department rather than for refuse collection, and was equipped with a 10 cwt. crane by the Chatteris Engineering Co. to enable the wagon to load itself with tramway rail and to discharge the rails at their destination. This wagon was turned out to Royal Show finish in steel grey, and lined in dark blue. The pair of wagons (Nos.103 and 104) for the Lancashire & Yorkshire Railway which followed it went as standard platform lorries in a livery of dark blue. Whilst these had complete bodies and cabs, in the case of the next wagon in numerical sequence - No.105 for Siddall & Hilton - Garretts were requested to supply only the ironwork for the body and cab leaving the woodwork to be done by the purchasers despite which, rather curiously, the chassis was specified to be painted in dark green and lined, though it would have seemed logical that the whole of the painting would have been done after the body and cab were complete. The wagon was intended for use by Siddall & Hilton's subsidiary firm, the Standard Wire Company at Sowerby Bridge, managed by Mr. Raymond Siddall. A letter he wrote in 1925, part of which is referred to in Chapter 8, throws interesting light on how the wagon was used. He wrote:

The body was made by a local body builder and is a tipper with 18 inch removable sides. It is far too heavy, especially the cab, the present unloaded weight being 4 tons 19 cwts, with sides etc. fixed.

The principal duty of the wagon was to carry coils of finished wire to the railway station and to return with coal or raw material. It ran mostly loaded, getting in about seven round trips of 3 miles each day. Besides the hills encountered on the public roads of that part of West Yorkshire the wagon had to traverse a steep slope of 1 in 4½ maximum gradient to reach the public road from the works. Experience of working it on such slopes led Mr. Siddall to say:

Personally I think all heavy motor lorries, especially Electrics which cannot use their motors as brakes, should have three independent sets of brakes, one of which should be on the front wheels, then there will be fewer accidents in hilly districts.

Other interesting points from his letter concerning the working of the wagon were:

The electric does not stand a chance with the petrol or steamer on long distances even if such distances are within the radius of the battery. Our electric would do 40 miles per charge easily on the level. The lead battery began to lose its capacity after two years' service but we continued to use it by the aid of boosts until three years were up - June, 1923. Then a 72 cell 300 ampere hour Nife was installed. This we expect to last longer and is now in use but we prefer to reserve comments on same until it has been given a fair test.

We have never been able to get a set of tyres to do 6 000 miles; they have usually got worn and cut up before that mileage was reached. One replace set was fitted in 1922 and a second set to the rear wheels this year (1925).

Charging is carried out by means of a water turbine driving a 21 KW generator. The switch board is fitted with an Igranic charging panel and meter readings are kept for costing purposes. In the cost given below electricity is charged at 1d per unit because this is the price fixed by our local Electricity Works. Actually we generate it cheaper than that as we have only depreciation and repairs to take into account, water power being free.

Costs of running this vehicle in 1923 were as follows:

	TOTAL COST	COST PER MILE
Wages	£135 18 0½	9¾d
Depreciation	122 8 11	8¾d
Insurance	10 0 3	¾d
Repairs	18 11 4	1¼d
Electricity @ 1d. per unit	30 1 6	2¼d
Tyres	17 12 6	1¼d
Sundries	5 16 3	½d
	£340 8 9½	2/0½d

During the period to which the costs refer the total number of miles travelled was 3370 and the total weight carried 2680 tons. As shown, the total cost per mile amounted to 2/0½d. and the cost per ton of goods carried 2/10¾d.

The conditions under which the vehicle is worked are, of course, by no means ideal and the cost figures would be bettered in many instances, but they are of interest as being figures obtained under adverse conditions. The hills the vehicle has to climb in its daily routine are exceedingly stiff - in fact we do not know of any similar vehicles working in a district like ours.

Another early No.5 wagon, No.106, supplied in October, 1919, to Morgans Brewery in Norwich, was painted in dark chocolate and had a plain platform with chockrails unlike No.144, also a No.5, delivered just over a year later to Mann, Crossman & Paulin, the London brewers, which had a brewers' body with typical latticed sides finished in the same middle green as other units in the owners' fleet. A further wagon supplied to a brewer was No.163 (July 1, 1921), a 1½-tonner sold to Nuttall & Co. (Blackburn) Ltd., Lion Brewery, Blackburn, for use by their mineral water department. Originally supplied with a 6 HP Vickers motor which ran into all kinds of problems, it was eventually re-equipped, at Garretts' expense, with a more reliable 80V Stowmarket built motor but this developed commutator trouble, bringing further protests from Nuttalls and much hand wringing in the Leiston Works management, which was all for denying liability and thereby, it hoped, incurring no further costs. Waters of AGE Motors handled it rather better. He simply rang up Nuttall's foreman fitter saying something on the lines of 'There's not much wrong but it would be a nuisance sending a fitter to Blackburn to put it right. I'll send another by rail for you to put in, and you can let me have the old one to repair here.' Nuttalls agreed at once and the matter was settled without further anguish.

The three No.3 wagons (Nos.108, 109, and 126) sent to Boots Pure Drug Co. between January and June, 1920, went as chassis only, a total contrast to the three No.3 wagons (127, 128, and 129) of November, 1921, supplied to the Savoy Hotel in London as vans for transporting linens between the hotel off the Strand and its laundry. The bodies had to afford complete protection for the contents both from the weather and from sneak thieves, but not at the expense of excessive weight. Those which the Leiston Thresher Department designed for this purpose managed to look stylish yet remained light. The necessary rigidity in them was obtained by a form of stressed skin construction in which a light skeleton framework of ash hoops 18" apart, braced and stiffened by lattice strips, was clad with hardwood 5-ply boarding ³/₈" thick. The roof was slightly domed to throw off water and was covered with painted canvas whilst the joints of the ply were covered with half round beading screwed on. Double doors were provided at the back with a latch, lock and key. The usable space in the bodies was 10' 3" long x 6' 0" wide x 6' 6" high.

Several of the pre-grouping railway companies displayed some interest in the use of battery electrics. The story of No.33119 (101) for the Great Eastern Railway has already been noted in Chapter 1, and passing references have been made to Nos. 107 and 108, both No.3 wagons, despatched in December, 1919, to the Great Northern, Great Central & Great Eastern Railways. What they were intended to be used for is to some extent speculative, but the parcel services in Lincoln, probably the only known example of willing co-operation between these three companies not otherwise noted for cordial relationships, seem a strong probability. The order was originally placed, or at least entered in Garretts' books, as being for five wagons. Nos.107 and 108 were the only two actually delivered, and even this pair, for some reason not known to me, were kept only for six months before being returned to their makers. The pre-group railways were notorious for being difficult customers to please, arrogance and caprice too often being displayed by some of their senior officers, spoiled, perhaps, by some seventy-five years of unbroken commercial success coupled with a virtual monopoly of long distance transport, soon to be assailed by road haulage. It may, indeed, be that caprice alone was the answer. On the other hand, if used in Lincoln they would have found it a difficult city since the fact that it is on two levels involves much hill climbing. As was noted in the 1919 report to the Garrett directors, sales staff had failed to size up properly the performances of which wagons were capable in a given terrain. Moreover railway bodywork was frequently heavy, leading to reduced performance, so that a combination of the two factors may have led to the rejection of 107 and 108. Nothing was really wrong with either as both were re-sold and had satisfactory working lives.

The other wagons supplied to pre-group railway companies were specials in diverse ways. No.121, for the Midland Railway Co. at Derby, was ordered through C.E.Holden of Manchester, so that the Works faced the dual problem of an exacting client ordering via an abrasive agent. As originally placed, the order required that the Garrett patent control gear cut out should be omitted and the controller connected direct to the operating handle with no spring catch or speed scale, though an entry in red ink on the memorandum book at the Works noted that Mr. Whitehurst, the railway company's inspecting engineer subsequently approved the fixing of a speed scale and spring catch. Another stipulation was that the spring shackles should be forged from $5/8$" plate rather than the standard $3/8$". Cowl ventilators on the battery covers were asked for. This vehicle was supplied as a bare chassis for the railway's own workshops to build the platform, cab and bodywork. In the numerical sequence, No.120 for the North Staffordshire Railway was the immediately preceding wagon. This, too, was ordered as a chassis only, to receive its purchaser's own style of bodywork. The main concern of Garretts in circumstances like this was that such bodies, as a rule, were designed on 'belt and braces' lines, and consequently were disproportionately heavy for the work they had to do, thus earning the chassis a poor reputation because the excess body weight reduced the mileage that could be accomplished on a single charge of the batteries.

The last of the pre-grouping railway companies to buy Garrett electrics was the London & South Western Railway which had four for use in the maintenance department at Southampton Docks. These were Nos. 137, 171, 177, and 178, all delivered within a fortnight in December, 1921, and January, 1922. They had electrically worked end tipping bodies constructed with chock rails as well as hinged sides and ends so that they could be used as platforms to carry barrels and drums. These were mostly to be seen in and around the dock area with occasional trips taking rubbish and debris to the tip. I suppose I probably saw them first about 1935 or 36, and I remember what curious old relics they appeared even then. The other memory I have is of the heedless and feckless way in which they were driven at full speed, admittedly probably only 8 - 10 miles per hour, over rough sett roadways and all kinds of minor obstacles, such as partly buried railway lines. They were 2½-tonners but were probably often loaded in excess of this limit. In November, 1926, soon after Tom Staulkey was made a service inspector, mainly for Garrett steam engines and wagons, he was asked to go to Southampton Docks to deal with a complaint concerning the condition of the bodies of wagons 177 and 178. It was said firstly that the tipping frame side members had bent and secondly, that because the bodies sat too low they were chafing on the main frame. Tom was a practical man to his finger tips, and his report is a dismissal by common sense of theoretical fault finding:

On examination of the above vehicles, I find that the Tipping Frame Girders are sprung up on the top edge where the Roller comes in contact with the stop block that causes the tipping. This bending runs along the girder from the stop block, and at that point is $3/8$" up running to practically nothing at the rear member of the Tipping Frame. This is on each side, and with each vehicle. There is no fracture visible in the girders and looks pressed up from the loads and rolling the load always coming heaviest at the stop block point.

The matter of the bodies setting too low is but very slight, and the knocking against the chassis is a wedge chafing over the top rib of bracket fixed on frame to carry the end bracket for tipping screw. The dropping is chiefly due to the wear of screw, nut, links and pins attached to tipping screw.

I saw both these Wagons tip their loads, and to my mind there is nothing they want to worry about, as giving these little clearances they will probably last as long as they have already done. One Vehicle has recently been overhauled and I suppose that is when they discovered the defect in the girder.

These Vehicles have been in constant use just on 4 years, and so far as I can gather, no one knows the exact load that has been put on them. The Wood Work is not in bad order considering the time, and nature of work they are doing.

Clearly he considered overloading and poor handling had been the main contributors to the state of the wagons rather than any design defect. Nevertheless parts were supplied as late as 1947.

Millers accounted for several wagons. Spillers & Bakers had No.139, a 2½-tonner, in August, 1921. This was turned out in Royal Show finish. The Sunderland millers E.C. Robson had Nos.133 and 134 (both 2½-tonners) through the agency of Christy Brothers & Co.Ltd. of Chelmsford in September, 1920. Both had a flat platform with a head board to protect the cab roof. These must have suited Robsons very well for subsequently they bought second-hand a further 2½-tonner (No.116 of June, 1920), originally a demonstrator in the hands of Currie & Co. in Newcastle and later sold to E.H.Vyse, who was a wholesale fish-merchant, from whom it went to Robsons. As noticed in Chapter 2 Hovis had No.267, another wagon that caused headaches to various Works people.

The 'high and narrow' appearance of the cab on earlier Garrett electrics clearly did not appeal to all. When No.174 (a No.5 wagon for a 3½-ton load) was put in hand on September 12, 1921, the standard specification 280 was amended to meet the requirements of a possible purchaser, Wm. Burgess (Bristol) Ltd., to whom the completed wagon was loaned on demonstration for a fortnight. The object of the changes, mainly in the cab, was to make it more like the competing GV vehicles in which the cab was only 5' 0" high. It was also required to be fitted with a two part glass windscreen, the upper portion of which was made to open. No sale resulted from this demonstration, and in July, 1922, the wagon was updated in the steering gear and fitted with the new eight speed Garrett controller. Even in this guise it found no purchaser, and lingered on in its makers' hands as a quasi-demonstrator until February, 1926, when it was sold as second-hand to Norwich Corporation for whom it was repainted and equipped with the kerbside controls devised by Mr. Collins, the Norwich Corporation's engineer. In this form it left the Works finally on April 24, 1926.

Though all the dealing with Local Authorities was not without its tribulations, delivery of 'E' type no.264 to Ipswich Borough Council in February, 1926, led to more complications than most. It is probable that as the Ipswich firm of Ransomes, Sims & Jefferies were competitive suppliers of such vehicles this led to political ripples in the council whilst local patriotism may have caused office and manual staff to be partisan. Whatever the underlying causes, early in April the Works received the following complaints concerning No.264:

[a]   It was slow on the road, making the three round trips take 45 minutes longer.

[b]   Its current consumption was too high, and as a result it could not run two days on one charge like the Ransomes No.5 wagon working alongside it.

Cyril Plane was deputed to go to Ipswich on April 19 to see what the real situation was. On presenting himself at the Health Department's Depot during the morning he was told the wagon was at work and would not be back until 1 p.m. so he decided instead to see Hicks, the Public Health Officer, who was responsible for the wagon. Clearly he was not impressed with the latter's qualifications for that task as he reported:

Mr. Hicks is not a technical man and hardly knows one end of the vehicle from the other; he has to obtain all his information from the driver and from the garage charge hand.

The specific complaints were [a] that a contact in the controller had become badly burned and had to be replaced at the expense of half a day's work by the wagon; and [b] that the tipping gear worked erratically. Later that day Plane looked at the tipping gear and found that the trouble was a nut on the body that could (and, therefore, sometimes did!) foul the operating lever in such a way that the return valve was held open to allow the hydraulic oil to pass straight back into the reservoir instead of working the ram. He showed the driver what was happening and arranged for a fresh lever to be sent with a set in it to clear the nut.

An examination of the battery charging log-book showed that the Garrett was using nearly 16% more current than the Ransomes. With regard to the speed Plane resolved on a practical test. When the wagon and its Ransomes companion set out from the depot for the afternoon round he rode with the Garrett. They both covered the 2.2 miles from the depot along Woodbridge Road to Britannia Road before diverging. In this distance the Ransomes gained on them by about 250 yards, mostly the result of the Garrett experiencing what Cyril Plane described as 'two slight traffic stops'. He observed 'it is difficult to find 45 minutes for three journeys at this rate.' He stayed with the wagon for the whole round, which was quite a long one as the area was thinly populated, and found that it took a total of 2 hours 6 minutes. The average speed out light was 7.35 m.p.h, and back loaded 7.1 m.p.h. The passengers in each case were the driver, four dustmen, Plane, and Marwood, his co-observer.

On his return he made it clear to Hicks that he felt there was little wrong with the wagon, but as Hicks was then engaged on writing up a report on it for the Committee, the burden of which was clearly intended to be dismissive of the Garrett, Plane secured from Hicks the promise that the wagon could be at their disposal for further tests on April 26 and 27. He obviously considered that the driver and other staff, for whatever reason, were prejudiced against it and that, properly managed, it could do what was required of it. His report on the events of those two days is interesting:

Report on visit to Ipswich, April 26th and 27th, re 3½-Ton Type E.T. Electric Vehicle

As instructed, I proceeded to Ipswich to obtain more data from the above vehicle.

Kemp, our driver, had arrived overnight, and as instructed, had adjusted the brakes and cleaned up the controller contacts. He also had the battery charged for two hours at the equalising rate on Sunday evening. The specific gravity the following morning was 1280 with the exception of one cell, which read 1265. (This cell was afterwards pointed out to the Chloride Battery Engineer, Mr. Nash, who promised to give it attention and get it back to normal working order.)

Monday morning the vehicle left the Garage for its usual district, and figures were taken to show the current consumption and average speed when both light and loaded, for the runs made during a complete battery discharge. It was ascertained that the loads carried and calls made throughout the tests were on a par with the usual work given to the Garrett vehicle.

The actual running times are given below and these show that the vehicle should do the work in the normal working hours viz. from 7.30 a.m. to 1 p.m. and 2 p.m. to 5 p.m. and it is not necessary to be 45 minutes late on the usual working day as we were informed.

RUN No.1. (Monday Morning)

	TIME	SPEEDOMETER READING MILES	AMP/HR. METER
Left Tramway Depot, Vehicle light	7.44	0	0
Stopped to commence collecting refuse	8.01	1.80	20
Finished loading	9.40	2.40	31
Commenced return journey with load	9.47	-	-
Arrived at Destructor	10.04	4.10	48

Load of refuse collected	2 tons 12 cwts 2 qrs nett.
Average Speed out Vehicle light	6.40 m.p.h.
Average Speed in Vehicle loaded	6.68 m.p.h.
Average A/hrs. per mile including Tip	11.90
Total number of stops whilst collecting	32

The district taken for this run was in and near Fuschia Lane. This made an uphill climb from the town and a downhill run most of the way back with the load.

The roads from which the collecting was done were of a moderate give and take nature, no severe hills being encountered, and all surfaces good and dry.

RUN No.2. (Monday Morning)

	TIME	SPEEDOMETER READING	AMP/HR METER
Left Destructor	10.15	4.10	49
Stopped to commence collecting refuse	10.31	5.80	74
Finished collecting	12.10	6.40	83
Departed for Destructor	12.13		
Arrived Destructor	12.26	7.80	99

Weight of refuse collected	2 tons 6cwts 2qrs nett
Average Speed out - Vehicle light	6.36 m.p.h.
Average Speed in - Vehicle loaded	6.47 m.p.h.
Average A/Hrs per mile including Tip	13.5
Total number of stops whilst collecting	23

The district same as in No.1 run with same road conditions.

RUN No.3 (Monday Afternoon)

	TIME	SPEEDOMETER READING	AMP/HR METER
Left Destructor	2.05	7.80	99
Stopped to commence collecting refuse	2.25	10.10	130
Finished collecting	4.20	11.60	150
Departed for Destructor	4.42	13.60	166

Weight of refuse collected	2 tons 8 cwts 0 qrs nett
Average Speed out - Vehicle light	6.90 m.p.h.
Average Speed in - Vehicle loaded	7.50 m.p.h.
Average A/Hrs per mile including Tip	11.50
Total number of stops whilst collecting	36.

This run was made along the Woodbridge Road, and two severe gradients were climbed whilst running out of the town light . The roads were in good condition, and all refuse collecting was done on the level. The return run with the load was over the same roads as the out run, coming down the two long gradients.

This concluded Monday's running, and the total current drawn from the battery was 166 A/Hrs. This amount Mr. Hicks informed me was 30 to 40 Amp/Hrs. less than that usually consumed by our vehicle on the same district. He was very pleased with the saving, and hoped we should be able to run the following morning without charging that evening.

The Specific Gravity of the battery had dropped to 1185 which appeared to be low for the amount of current used. I therefore phoned up Mr. Nash to obtain his opinion on the matter. After explaining the position to this gentleman, he informed me that the battery should give another 100 ampere hours without recharging, but the gravity might perhaps drop to 1120 or thereabouts, and this was not good for the battery, and it would not do to make it a continual practice. He would not definitely say why the gravity had dropped so low in this case, but thought perhaps it was because the cells had never been completely discharged.

No definite comparative information could be obtained as to the district the vehicle would be on during the following morning, and as 99A/Hrs had been used Monday morning, it was decided to take the risk and run without charging.

On Tuesday morning the first trip was run with the battery voltage almost normal, but after leaving the destructor, and proceeding through the town, with the Vehicle light for the second trip, the voltage suddenly dropped, and on the slight incline in Princess St. opposite Frazers it dropped to 45 volts.

The vehicle at once turned back and the battery gave out just sufficient current to reach the garage. A boosting charge was given for 30 minutes at 130 amps. and this was sufficient to complete the second journey.

In the lunch hour the battery was again boosted, and this enabled the vehicle to complete the day's work, without putting Mr. Hicks to any inconvenience.

Therefore only four trips totalling 19.6 miles were obtained for the one charge for a current consumption of 250 A/Hrs.

RUN No.4 (Tuesday Morning)

	TIME	SPEEDOMETER READING	AMP/HRS METER
Left Destructor	7.45	13.70	170
Stopped to commence collecting refuse	8.50	15.90	205
Finished collecting	10.00	17.40	228
Departed for Destructor	10.10	-	-
Arrived at Destructor	10.26	19.70	250
Weight of refuse collected	2 tons 10 cwts 2 qrs nett		
Average Speed of Vehicle out light	6.60 m.p.h.		
Average Speed of Vehicle in loaded	7.90 m.p.h.		
Average A/Hrs per mile including Tip	13.30		

On this run the refuse was collected from Back Hamlet and Camden Road, which necessitated a long uphill climb with the vehicle light, and a steady downhill run for a considerable distance on the return journey. A road of very loose and soft construction about 150 yards long was traversed whilst collecting.

A series of readings were obtained on the level (see below) and on the main gradients. On enquiring at the Surveyor's Office at the County Hall, I found that only the value of the main gradients in the town were logged, only two of which our vehicle had climbed, and further, these two were given over the total length of the gradient, and not of the various surfaces comprising it.

Average of seven readings taken on the level with Vehicle light	Volts	85
	Amps	57.50
	Average Speed	9.55 m.p.h.
Average of seven readings taken on the level with Vehicle loaded	Volts	80.30
	Amps	74
	Average Speed	8.01 m.p.h.

The vehicle appears to coast better this week with the load but there is no improvement with the vehicle light.

I had a straight talk with the driver, and told him in an unoffensive manner that he was prejudiced against the vehicle, and that most of his complaints were ridiculous. He did not have much to say, but soon lost his sullen manner and in the afternoon he was most affable.

He told me that the vehicle was on one of the hardest routes of the lot, and that many houses had recently been built and added to his district since the Ransome vehicles used to run two days per charge. (Note:- The batteries in the Ransome vehicles are now in their third year, and are not expected to run the two days.) He did not think this would be the reason for all our heavy consumption, but suggested that it was a contributory cause.

On Tuesday afternoon Mr. Little told me that the members of the Committee who opposed the Garrett Vehicle were asking why it was not giving the service he had told them it would. It appears he had told them exactly what Mr. Montgomery had led him to believe, viz: that the Vehicle would give a higher speed, and a lower current consumption than the Ransome, because it was up-to-date in every respect.

Mr. Little had advised them to buy the Garrett Vehicle, although the price was above Ransomes, and it meant the work leaving the town.

He stated that another vehicle will be required shortly, but was afraid this would have to be a Ransome.

Note:- The lubricator on the back end of the Armature bearing of the main motor has been lost, and one of the Kingfisher type recently sent for the Front Axle Pivot Pin has been broken by the Speedometer Gear wheel hitting it.

Cyril Plane's estimate of the true situation was accurate. Future electric vehicle purchases in Ipswich were made from Ransomes.

Once the controller problems had been overcome the Garrett electrics became very reliable machines and many had long lives. For example, the fleet of twenty used by Sheffield, the most recent of which dated from 1924, lasted until 1945. No doubt the shortage of new vehicles in the 1939-45 war contributed to their longevity but, for whatever reason, it was a creditable record helped by the fact that they had been converted to run on pneumatic tyres, beginning with No.248, which was so equipped in February, 1935. Spare parts probably continued to be supplied for some vehicles until the early 1950's as the original blue prints for certain components were used so much that they had to be replaced by new ones, the latest of which was dated 1952.

Fig.47. *The only Garrett electric used in the fish trade was No.116 (June, 1920) owned by E.H. Vyse of North Shields. Originally sent to Currie & Co. of Newcastle as a demonstrator, out of deference to the climate of the area it had a glass windscreen and high cab doors (but without glass). It was unique in having a bumper bar at the front. After five years with Vyse it went to E.C.Robson & Sons, the Sunderland millers.*

Fig.48. *The 'G' type with worm drive set the style for what was hoped to be a new era of Garrett battery electrics, but its success was shortlived. This is No.266 for Boots Pure Drug Co. of Nottingham who commissioned the good-looking bodywork themselves.*

Fig.49. *No.236 delivered in February, 1924, to the City of Sheffield was the tipping version of the 'G' type. Hydraulic tipping in place of the 'roll-back and tip' type enabled the loading line to be lowered, though not sufficiently.*

Fig.50. *No.242, the solitary example of the articulated version of the 'G', went to the City of Norwich in July, 1924.* [S.R.O.]

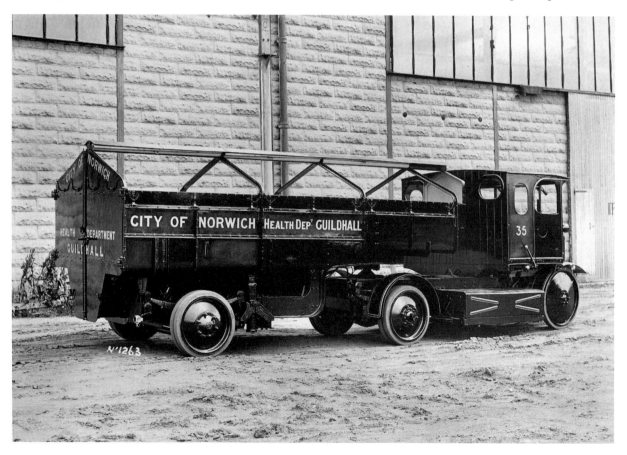

Fig.51. *C2-type No.263 photographed in the Top Works showing how the motor and worm-driven rear axle were arranged, and also the kerbside controls.* [S.R.O.]

Fig.52. *The only known photograph to show A.J. Serve (extreme left) posed on Leiston Station with Col. Garrett (in bowler hat), Livesay ((briefly Works Manager - left rear) and a party of five, all unidentified, from Glasgow Corporation.*

Fig.53. *No.261, the first Garrett trolley bus, outside the Charles Roe works in Leeds after having the body fitted.* [S.R.O.]

Fig.54. *An early duty was to demonstrate on the Keighley system. Note that in this picture it had the original trolley pole base - a bought in component.*

Chapter 4

The Trolley Buses

The vicissitudes of the market for the steam powered products of Leiston Works, particularly for the undertype steam wagons, the story of which was narrated in Part 2, acted as a constant spur to the board of Richard Garrett & Sons Ltd. to sell other types of products that would boost the flagging turnover. The limited market for battery driven electrics had failed to provide sufficient additional production to meet the need and, moreover, even the sales of these vehicles were in decline.

Although the underlying expertise of the Leiston drawing office and of its chief draughtsman and designer, Maurice Plane, lay in steam and mechanical engineering, the work that A.J.Serve and his helpers had put into the battery vehicle designs had demonstrated that within it the capability existed to tackle other and more complex electric vehicle projects. Maurice Plane was recalled to me as having had an excellent working relationship with Serve, nominally his subordinate but whom, in electrical matters, he treated as an equal. W.H. (Bill) Deane who worked with Serve as the other half of the team was also an extremely good electric vehicle man. After Serve's departure (c.1928) Deane took over the electric vehicle section, being described as 'our chief electrical vehicle designer' but, in reality, by that time he was the sole member of it, dealing with the electrical matters whilst other sections of the work were dealt with as part of the general business of the drawing office, other drawing help being co-opted on the mechanical aspects.

As far as trolley buses were concerned the undoubted boardroom initiator was Col. Frank Garrett, always the convinced advocate of electric vehicles. In this he was some two generations ahead of his time - a 'green', so to speak, sixty years before the movement gained coherence. He had friends in the upper echelons of business and manufacturing in Ipswich. Municipal transport in Ipswich, centred on the tramway system, had potentially serious financial problems, and would have been faced with the necessity for a fleet renewal and extensive track-works had the tramways remained in use. On the other hand the fixed electric side of the system, the generating capacity, distribution mains and overhead equipment, which represented a substantial part of the total capital investment, remained in good order. During 1924 the debate about the future of the town transport system became very hotly contested, some advocating the retention of trams, others pressing for petrol buses as replacements whilst a third group canvassed the cause of the trolley bus (to use, as is done throughout this chapter, Garrett's spelling rather than present usage) or 'trackless tram' as it was often referred to at that time. As an aid to a solution of the problems it was resolved to commission a report from Alfred Baker, general manager of the Birmingham Corporation Tramways Department which, notwithstanding its name, had routes operated variously by trams, trolley buses, and motor buses. His report, delivered in 1925, advocated that Ipswich should convert its system to trolley buses, thereby continuing to use the electricity generating and distribution facilities already existing for the trams. The report was adopted by Ipswich Corporation, thus creating a demand for trolley buses more or less upon the Garrett doorstep. The intense local interest that had been generated and had culminated in Baker's report had, in the meantime, presented Col. Garrett with a powerful boardroom case for taking up this new and, in his view, promising branch of electric vehicle manufacture. If, he had argued, Ransomes, Sims & Jefferies, their long-standing but friendly rivals, were likely to be building rolling stock for such revivified undertakings why should not Garretts take part also? Though it may have been convenient to use the Ipswich case as a local example to sway his board it is doubtful if his own favourable opinion of the project was so narrowly based. Tram replacement was under consideration in many locations besides Ipswich whilst pioneer cities such as Bradford had been using trolleys since as early as 1911. Whilst it is not possible to embark here upon a review of the situation as it existed nationally and internationally in 1924 it can be said that the advocacy of trolley bus manufacture did seem to be based on a sound foundation of economics. Though the trade in battery electrics had faltered its legacy was an able design team, a satisfactory electric vehicle department in the Works and a good name with Garretts' municipal clients. In this running discussion Victor Garrett was firmly in agreement with his eldest brother; Alfred Garrett normally disagreed with him only in private and invariably backed him up in the boardroom; Bennett, the AGE nominee to the board was non-committal but was persuaded. How W.J. Marshall reacted to the matter Victor did not recall, but the chairman's proposal was carried, and work on the new venture was set in train.

Fig.55. A further picture of No.261 on the turning circle at Ingrow, Keighley. By the time this picture was taken the bus had acquired a new trolley base of Serve's own design.

Fig.56. Back view of No.261, showing the emergency door and the retractable seat fixed to it. The photo was taken whilst it was at Keighley.

The preparation of the design for the first trolley bus, designated 'Class S' and intended to serve as a demonstrator, began early in 1924, though the actual date is not recorded. More or less finished drawings of trolley buses began with ZA139 which showed the general arrangement of a 30-seater 'railless' proposal for Ashton-under-Lyme, dated April 11, 1924, to which ZA141 also referred. Drawing ZA140 showed a 38-seater, and ZA147 a 36-seater, whilst ZA149 related to the frame sections and bending moments of a 'railless' bus. A scheme for a 36-seater for Wigan Corporation was shown on ZA158 but the first drawing using the designation 'S' is No.159, a general arrangement dated September 22, 1924, but it is likely that this followed rather than preceded the experimental construction work in the shops. Repeated use of the term 'railless' leads one to surmise that Serve may have taken a long look at the *Railless* designs in use in Birmingham and Ipswich before beginning his own layout. As must have been virtually obligatory, he turned for the 50HP motor to Bull Motors Ltd, fellow members of the AGE group. The chassis was pressed out of 32/38 ton high tensile steel, the side and all other members ¼" thick, except for the centre cross member which was $^{7}/_{32}$" thick. These were a bought-in component, either from Macintosh or Rubery Owen, though at the latter part of the production run they were made in the boiler shop. Why it was decided to put the initial demonstrator on solid tyres is not known. Possibly the opinions of Alfred Baker may have had some bearing on the matter as the *Railless* buses in use by his own organisation at Birmingham all ran on solids, and solid tyres were subsequently adopted for the trolley buses purchased by Ipswich as a result of his report. The new vehicle was allocated the Works No.261, following the 5-ton GT type refuse collectors for Norwich Corporation. This places the date of commencement at about August, 1924. The bare chassis was erected in late November and early December. The body fitted was a 32-seater (though the registration referred to it as a 35-seater and the order book as a 37-seater) with central entrance and rear emergency door. The seating was upholstered in leather. The wheels, made at Leiston, were of pressed steel disc type to receive 1085 x 185 Dunlop solid tyres, single at the front but twins at the rear. All wheels ran on Timken roller bearings, which had proved so successful on the undertype steam wagons. The body was built by Chas. H.Roe (1923) Ltd. of Crossgates, Leeds, and the completed bus was registered by Serve in Leeds with the number UM 1755, on June 30, 1925, when it was referred to in the registration particulars as a 'trackless bus'. Painted in a bright red with cream upper works, it was a striking looking vehicle. The equipment of the bus was, by the standards of its time, reasonably complete, including a speedometer, a fire extinguisher, Sheppee or similar tyre chains for the rear wheels, and a Berkshire windscreen wiper. An anomaly was that it was provided with a mechanical gong, as well as a horn, for a warning device. It was braked only at the rear wheels. In 1925/26 the design of bus braking was at a point where two wheeled brakes were still legally acceptable but where virtually all those close to the actual operation of buses were aware that the braking of all axles was a most desirable improvement. Thus, although two wheel brakes remained nominally the standard specification for Garrett 'O' types, in practice few were supplied in this mode.

Victor Garrett had been given the task of overseeing the sales of the trolley buses for which purpose he recruited W.H.(Harry) Keys as his salesman. Keys was the cousin of Nelson Keys, the stage comedian, now largely forgotten. Harry revelled in the connection and was not averse to allowing it to be thought that he was Nelson's brother. Always cheerful and optimistic, not bad qualities in a salesman, he was also an irrepressible practical joker, a trait that tended to pall, particularly with his victims. Serve, a very serious, not to say doleful, man, became increasingly cast for that part. Victor described Keys to me as one who revelled in expense account living. In the year ending March 31, 1926, Harry was paid a salary of £500. 0s. 0d. plus a sales commission of £25. 0s. 0d. but received also £362 0s. 0d. for expenses.

To demonstrate the 'S'-type permission was obtained to run it on the overhead of the Leeds undertaking which had been installed since 1911. By 1925 the Leeds vehicles were heavily out of date, and it was hoped that replacements might be Garrett-built. It was, however, a firmly pro-tram city and trolley bus operation was dropped in 1928 in favour of tramway extensions. In July and August, 1925, further demonstrations were held in Keighley where, again, trolley buses had been used since 1911. The runs on July 10 were well attended and reported upon but Keighley itself bought nothing, though against this failure to impress the local administrations must be set the fact that as a result of witnessing what was achieved by the prototype at Leeds and Keighley, the managements of the Ipswich, Bradford, and Grimsby transport departments all placed orders - Ipswich for fifteen, Bradford for four, and Grimsby for five. Some trouble seems to have been experienced with the motor whilst it was on demonstration at Keighley as there is a note in the order book that says:

> Bull Motors to be asked to send a man to alter the packing behind the pole pieces back to what it was before the motor was altered in Keighley in August, 1925.

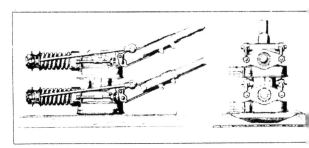

Fig.57. *Detail of No.261 showing the central entrance and the superimposed type trolley pole mounting.*

Fig.58. *Drawing of the trolley pole mounting.*

Fig.59. No.262 at Strachan & Brown's works, in the livery of Ipswich Corporation for demonstration purposes. [S.R.O.]

Keys had learned to drive the bus whilst it was in Leeds, and had found a new means to torment Serve by cutting the motor in such a way as to simulate a breakdown. This would bring Serve racing to the front of the bus to find Harry Keys laughing at his own joke, whereupon he would shake his head, exclaiming sadly, 'Meester Keys, Vy do you play zees tricks on me?'

The 'S' class demonstrator remained solitary for, as a result both of the observations of the Garrett personnel present and of the requirements of the prospective purchasers, a number of amendments were made in subsequent vehicles. The most noticeable of these was the deepening of the body panels to bring the lower edge below the chassis line. Serve was able to lower the floor line several inches by cranking the frames over the axles. In the mechanical and electrical arrangements nothing material was altered. It was sold finally to Bradford Corporation for whom it was converted to run on pneumatics though it retained its red livery which earned it the nick-name of 'the fire-engine'. Bradford required it to be delivered without its indicator, the mechanical gong, the fire extinguisher, number plates, screen wiper, speedometer, wheel chains, or trolley gear, doubtless wishing to fit their own. A second bus, numbered 262, was begun soon after No.261, but completion was deferred until the Leeds and Keighley trials of No.261 had taken place, enabling it to be completed to the amended design which was designated the 'O'-type. This bus remained in hand, used for demonstration, until the end of November, 1926, when it too was delivered to Bradford Corporation. Its final duty as a demonstrator was at Mexborough where the Mexborough & Swinton Traction Co. were looking for trolley buses suitable for replacing their trams. From Mexborough it went direct to Bradford. This bus had a centre entrance body by Strachan & Brown of Acton, London W3. Unlike No.261 it had four-wheel brakes. When new it seems to have been with Ipswich on an extended trial or hire basis, and appeared in Ipswich green livery at the 1925 Commercial Motor Exhibition but was subsequently repainted in the then new blue livery of Leeds City Transport, even down to the City crests. Whilst on demonstration runs in Leeds early in 1926 it was filmed for publicity purposes. The film came to light in the Drawing Office store (the 'dead-house') among rubbish during our researches in the early 1960's and it was drawn to the attention of John Huntley who had a copy made which is lodged in the National Film Archive.

The Ipswich buses, the bodies of which were also built by Strachan & Brown, were required to have entrances at both front and rear, as a result of which the seating came down to thirty places, and the front axle had necessarily to be moved back. The first of the Ipswich series to be completed was numbered 273 and was ready for delivery on March 3, 1926, to be followed by Nos.274 and 276 a month later, though No.275 did not go until May 4, and the last was sent on August 16. This, it will be remembered, was the year of the General Strike and of the long coal strike, both of which impeded production. On the Ipswich order the brakes reverted to rear axle only, with two sets of shoes in each drum, the foot brake set air operated from equipment supplied by British Air Brakes Ltd., incorporating an electric compressor, and the other set actuated by the hand brake lever. These buses had 50HP motors. The solid tyres were 140 for 771mm. at the front and a twin 120 for 850mm. on the rear. Because of the front entrance the wheelbase was 13' 6", compared with 15' 6" on No.262. A ten speed controller was fitted. To be standard with the buses Ipswich had ordered from Ransomes Sims & Jefferies the bodies were equipped with 'Resistance' seating, whilst the direction indicators, klaxon horns and signal bells were supplied by the customer.

A bus intended to bear the number 288 was put in hand on January 29, 1926, for use as a demonstrator. This was to have had four wheel brakes with one rear set of shoes equipped for Westinghouse air operation, but probably because of the politically and socially unsettled climate of the year and concern at the capital being tied up in stock and demonstrators the order was cancelled on April 13, 1926, and the material made up to that time was used to build No.300, the first car for Grimsby. The work on this batch for Grimsby ran concurrently with the latter part of the Ipswich order and also with an order to supply buses to Copenhagen. How this order for Copenhagen was obtained is not entirely clear. The Garrett demonstration at Leeds and Keighley had attracted a gratifying degree of attention which Keys, notwithstanding his tiresome addiction to practical jokes and double whiskies on the firm, had followed up conscientiously. When I discussed this with Victor Garrett he mentioned a Continental demonstrator bus, but I think he may have become confused with the original 'S'-type demonstrator as the Continental demonstrator was not built until late summer or autumn, 1928. A photograph, Fig.81, taken in the Station Works shows the virtually completed left-hand drive demonstrator alongside No.40 of the Mexborough & Swinton series which was finished on October 26, 1928. However, this is a digression. Whatever the circumstances, the order from Nordsjøellands Elektricitets og Spørvejs Aktieselkab in Copenhagen, for

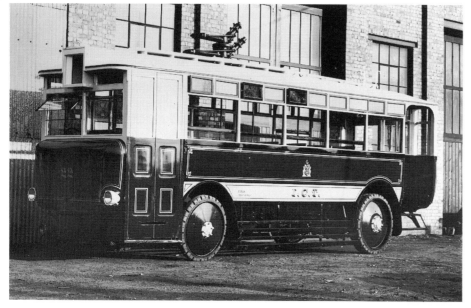

Fig.60. Ipswich No.22, with front entrance body. [S.R.O.]

Fig.61. (below left) Interior of No.21, looking forward.
Fig.62. (below right) Similar view in a Grimsby car.
[both S.R.O.]

Fig.63. West Hartlepool car No.25, bodied by Roe.

delivery in 1926, was for five chassis, fitted with bodies from Strachan & Brown. All were completed between August 4 and September 22, 1926, and carried the Works Nos. 306 to 310 inclusive. These buses had rear entrances and, at peak times on Summer Sundays, were intended to haul Arato type trailers (see Part 2) with locally built central entrance bodies. A further three chassis (Works Nos.335, 336, and 337) were supplied in June and July, 1927, but these were fitted with bodies in Denmark. The trolley arms to all the buses were supplied and fitted by the customer as also were switches for lighting and heating.

A batch of twelve with central entrances, bearing the numbers 312 to 323 inclusive, went to West Hartlepool between the end of January and the middle of March, 1927. These differed from standard in having a wheelbase of 14' 10", and four-wheel brakes, and were bodied by Roe. There followed three buses, Nos.325, 326, and 327, for Bradford, all more or less 'standard' except for having four-wheel brakes. These, too, were bodied by Roe, but on the other hand the four (Nos.328 to 331 inclusive) supplied to St.Helens Corporation in May, 1927, for the Prescot to Rainhill route all had 36-seater bodies by Ransomes, Sims & Jefferies Ltd, in which the body-builders' drawing office had clearly had a major role. The destination blind was moved from the centre front to nearside front; the windows were arranged three on each side of the central entrance; the upper lights were the same width as the windows below them and were bottom hung to open inwards; the front apron was of a modified design, and a five rail life preserver was fitted at the front. In my opinion these were the best looking of any of the buses supplied by Garretts. The companions of this batch through the Works were Nos.332 and 333, completed on April 24 and May 24 respectively, and destined for Grimsby Corporation. Notwithstanding the fact that Grimsby had specified front entrances for their cars they insisted upon a 15' 6" wheelbase, compared with the 14' 6" normal to front entrance cars, which meant amending the side members of the main frame. The Hartlepool contract was unique, so far as I am aware, in that the conversion of the fixed overhead conductor system from single to double was also a part of the Garrett contract, though the work was sub-let in its entirety to R.W. Blackwell & Co. Ltd.

In 1926 Col. Garrett visited the AGE sales organisation in South America. Clayton & Shuttleworth of Lincoln, who had supplied many straw-burning traction engines to Argentina, were in terminal decline, and his accurate appraisal of this situation enabled the order for the 80 BHP direct ploughing engines for Argentina to be secured. Another product of the visit was the opportunity to supply the so-called 'Chile portables' which briefly revived the dwindling output of portables at Leiston. In the direct line of the present narrative he was instrumental in securing an order from the tramway undertaking in Lima, Peru, for six single-decked buses bearing bodies by Roe which took the Works Nos. 338 to 343 inclusive. Like the Ipswich and Grimsby cars they were of the short wheelbase type with front loading doors, but unlike the former, the South American vehicles had a door in the centre of the rear. In deference to the high temperatures encountered in Lima a double ceiling was installed, finished internally in bird's-eye maple. The top hopper ventilators were operated by the conductor, all on each side being connected to cranks on a common operating rod. The windows were given the maximum possible depth of opening and green sunblinds were fitted internally. The general standard of finish of the bodies was high. The internal panels below the waistline were veneered in English oak; cover strips and moulding were in mahogany, and all the hardwood was polished. The window openings had the corners radiused by the use of aluminium castings. The air inlet for motor ventilation was inside the body to minimise intake of dust. Uniquely as far as the Garrett output was concerned the bodies were painted white all over relieved with moss green. The group were all provided with four-wheel brakes. The foot brake and the Westinghouse air brakes worked on all wheels - the hand brake, as usual, on the rear only. Unusually the springs came from Jonas Woodhead & Co. whereas most had been by John Brown of Sheffield.

The cars were intended for an intensely worked 6.73 km. route from Malambito to Cocharcas with a headway of 6 minutes and thirty-seven stops. Taken with poor road surfaces this was expected to be punishing to the vehicles which were ordered with a very large quantity of spares. Rumour has it that their working life was only some four years. In the turbulence of Peruvian politics the undertaking was nationalised in the mid-thirties. What happened to the cars at that time is not known but in *Trolleybus Magazine* for January/February, 1988, there was a photograph of a tram in October, 1946, the body of which was clearly taken from one of the trolley buses.

The final customer to place a considerable order for 32-seater single-decker trolley buses was the Mexborough & Swinton Traction Co. whose tramway conversion became effective in 1929. An initial

Fig.64. The entire West Hartlepool fleet (Works Nos.312 to 323inc.), all with Roe bodies, outside the tramway offices when newly delivered.

Fig.65. An unidentified NESA car at Strachan & Brown's works. [S.R.O.]

Fig.66. (below) NESA Car No.1 (Works No.306) on a demonstration run in Copenhagen showing the separate mountings of the trolley poles requested by the clients.

batch of six (Works Nos.379 - 384 inclusive - Mexborough & Swinton Nos.34 - 39) were delivered between December 31, 1927, and February 14, 1928. The initial batch of six had 50 HP motors but these turned out to be somewhat underpowered, and subsequently the 60 HP motor was fitted to the rest of the order. The initial six were converted in two batches of three finished on April 30 and July 4, 1929, respectively. In the same rebuild they were given the Bull eddy brake. All had the standard central entrance and, although it is not absolutely certain who bodied them, the probability is that the work was done at Leiston. The second batch numbering twenty-one in all left the Works, as completed, between the end of October, 1928, and the end of February, 1929. On these, the bodies were certainly made at Leiston Works, the appearance differing in details from the initial six. A further batch of three (Nos.425 - 427), similarly bodied, but without the glazed ventilators above the transom (louvred steel vent panels taking their place), followed in May and June, 1930, the last buses to be built at Leiston. The change in ventilators did not do much for their appearance but probably helped production costs, and certainly made them safer. These latter three, at least, had twin 35 HP motors plus the Bull eddy brake. Col. A.C.Trench, the inspecting engineer of the Ministry of Transport, visited Mexborough on November 20, 1928, to view the working of the eddy braking system and prepared a report as follows:

I have the honour to report, for the information of the Minister of Transport, that while at Mexborough on the 20th November, 1928, I inspected the new Eddy current electrical brake which has been fitted to a number of Garrett 4-wheel single deck trolley buses in use there.

This brake has been constructed by the makers of the (Bull) motor used on these vehicles on the suggestion of Mr. McGibbon, the Tramways Manager. It is not yet fully protected but as soon as this is done Messrs. Garrett will send plans and full particulars.

Generally speaking it consists of a disc suitably ventilated mounted on a front extension of the motor shaft, in which, when rotating, eddy currents are generated by magnet poles excited by the trolley wire current (not by current regenerated from the motor as is the case of a tramcar magnetic brake). This has the obvious disadvantage that it fails in case of dewiring and therefore any such braking device must be supplemented by ample emergency brake capacity.

On the other hand control of line current is easier and from a short trial it seems to provide a very sweet and effortless service brake of ample power for such work, retardation of about 5 ft. per sec. per sec. being obtained with this brake alone on a fully laden car.

The application of the brake is effected by the foot brake pedal which controls a rheostat in the brake circuit. After it is fully applied further movement of the brake pedal applies the ordinary brakes to the rear wheel drums. The hand brake also operates on the rear wheel drums. The front wheel brakes on these vehicles have been abolished concurrently with the fitting of these eddy current brakes.

These brakes have been in use for some months on nine vehicles with very satisfactory results, and they are now to be fitted to the remainder of the Company's fleet. I was informed that the heating effect after 17 hours continuous service use produced a rise of only 56°F in the brake field coils and the full application only absorbed about 1 k.w. from the line. The saving in wear and maintenance of brake drums is very material. The additional heating of the motor by the proximity of the disc is stated to be negligible.

I think that in the case of these single deck vehicles of comparatively moderate weight the abolition of front wheel brakes is not seriously objectionable, and the arguments as to the extra care and attention needed for maintenance and adjustment of such brakes impressed me, but with a heavier vehicle, whatever system of braking is applied, the ultimate point of application is between the tyre and the road and it is evident that in such cases the use of front wheel brakes utilises the additional adhesion of the weight on the front wheels.

It must be remembered also that there are disadvantages about the use of a brake on the driving shaft as compared with direct application to the wheel drums, though these disadvantages are not so serious in the case of an easily regulated brake of moderate power intended for service use, such as this eddy current brake in question.

At the same time these vehicles have been fitted with B.T.H. contactor type control which seemed to be well arranged and satisfactory.

I recommend that these alterations be approved provisionally and that the Company should be asked to submit a report on the working of the brake after six months use.

One further single-decker remains to be mentioned. This was No.392 built in the summer of 1928 as a left-hand drive for use as a demonstrator at De Bilt near Utrecht early in 1929 on the occasion of the congress of the Netherlands Light Railway & Tramway Association. Despite predictions that the Dutch tramway network was ripe for conversion no sales took place and the bus was repatriated. Later in 1929 it was used as Garrett's exhibit at the annual conference of the Municipal Tramways & Transport Association at Great Yarmouth between September 11 and 13. As Great Yarmouth had only a single wire overhead it was forced to use its skate for demonstration runs. After standing for a long period at the Station Works it was rebuilt to right-hand drive and sold, at a bargain price, to Ipswich in November, 1931. As has been narrated in Part 2, the always bleak financial situation at the Works had become desperate by that time, and any venture that would turn stock into cash was considered.

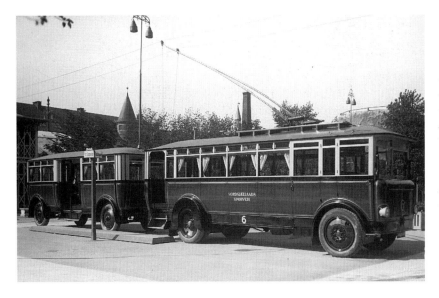

Fig.67. NESA Car No.6 (Works No.335), the first of the second batch, shown with one of the Arato type trailer buses used at weekends.

Fig.68. (below) Rear end view of the same car. Air brakes were fitted to both car and trailer.

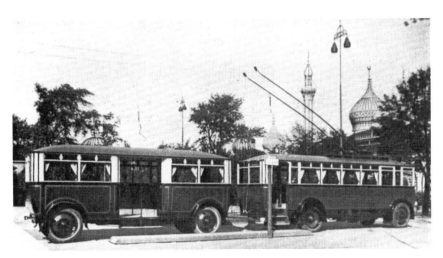

Fig.69. (L to R) Cars 1 to 4, (Works Nos. 328-331 inc.) supplied to St.Helens Corporation in May, 1927, with bodies by Ransomes, Sims & Jefferies.

In the meantime, however, a new development had taken place. Outline drawings were prepared for various double-deckers. Drawing ZA191, dated August 24, 1925, showed a double-decker with a body by Ransomes, intended for Ipswich, whilst ZA193, dated a day or so later, was for a 50 seater with a body by Roe for the same prospective purchaser. In the autumn of 1925 outline general arrangements with no potential clients' names attached were done for 57 seater and 54 seater double-deckers, supposedly on six wheels. Attracted by the increased carrying capacity offered in single-decked buses by the then burgeoning vogue for six-wheeled chassis the design was developed for a six-wheeled single-decker to be built on an experimental or stock footing. The first mention of work upon the drawing for this bus occurs in the Drawing Office weekly summary of work done during week ending November 30, 1926. The order to the Works to begin manufacture was dated February 2, 1927. At an early stage in the construction of the body the decision was taken to change the design to an open staircase double-decker with saloon upper deck, the instruction to the Works asking that body components already made for the single-deck body should be re-used in the double-decker 'as far as possible'. Though I cannot find a note of the date of completion the bus is known to have appeared at the Commercial Motor Show in November, 1927. It was given the Works No.387. Whilst this was going on Doncaster Corporation had put in hand the conversion of its Bentley tram route to trolley bus operation, the work to the fixed part of the system being carried out by Clough, Smith & Co. Ltd. Despite the fact that Clough Smith had a working arrangement with Karrier of Huddersfield, Garretts, probably in the person of Harry Keys, had managed to obtain an invitation to tender for vehicles and had secured a contract for four. These were to be double-decked 60-seaters on six-wheeled chassis. Whether or not the double-decked demonstrator had played a part in securing this order is not known.

The braking of the twin rear axles of these Doncaster double-deckers led to problems with the Ministry of Transport who, while quite willing to approve the coupling of the levers together by rods, looked askance at the suggestion of the Doncaster Transport Manager, T. Potts, that each wheel should have its own Westinghouse air brake cylinder supplemented by an emergency brake on the transmission operated by a ratchet lever. Pragmatism came to the rescue. Potts was allowed to have two of the Karrier buses completed as he wished, whereupon a practical test convinced the Ministry inspector, Col. Trench, that his proposals were safe and effective. All four of the Garretts were thus equipped from the beginning. The bodies by Charles Roe with which these four buses were fitted had enclosed rear staircases and had about them the imprint of their builders' practice. In service the four proved not to be the equal of the Karriers running on the same service and were not added to. They were, however, made the central subject in the Garrett publicity film now in the National Film Archive. The Doncaster buses carried the Works Nos. 385, 386, 388, and 389, the last leaving the Works in mid-April, 1928. All were withdrawn, after relatively short lives, in 1935/36.

Other double-deckers were supplied to Southend-on-Sea Corporation for use on their two mile route from the Kursaal via Marine Parade, Harlington Road, and High Street to Priory Park. This had been run without conspicuous success by four-wheeled single-deckers on solid tyres, but the new vehicles for which Garretts secured the order were to be six-wheeled double-deckers. The first of these was No.387, the demonstrator, which was delivered on a hire basis in January, 1928, and purchased at the end of February, 1929, taking the fleet number 104, the only one to be supplied with an open staircase. The remaining five (Nos.414 to 418 inclusive) were delivered in May and June, 1929, and all had bodies built at Leiston Works with enclosed staircases. These lasted longer than the Doncaster buses but were withdrawn in 1939.

The catalogue of the firm's unsuccessful tenders for trolley buses makes interesting reading. During 1927 they prepared outline arrangements for single-deckers for home authorities at Chesterfield, Ashton-under-Lyme, and Hastings, and overseas operators in Bloemfontein, Georgetown (Penang), and Tokyo, whilst double-deckers were tendered for at Maidstone and Chesterfield. The list for 1929 and 1930 included single-deckers for Darlington, Hull, Rotherham, Kyoto (Japan), Christchurch (New Zealand), and Liège (Belgium) with schemes for double-deckers for the Warrington, Pontypridd, and South Lancashire undertakings. It seems, too, that having embarked successfully upon their building of bodies for trolley buses they went at least as far as the submission of outline drawings for bodies to be mounted onto petrol engined chassis (mostly Thornycroft but at least one on a Leyland *Titan)*. The earliest of these (drawing ZA396) was for a 32-seater for Exeter, and was dated October 27, 1928, and the last (ZA467, dated November 4, 1929) a 32-seater to suit an unspecified chassis for Aberdeen. Unfortunately the drawings

Figs. 70 to 73.
Cars 2 and 4 of the Lima undertaking in carefully posed scenes when they were newly delivered.

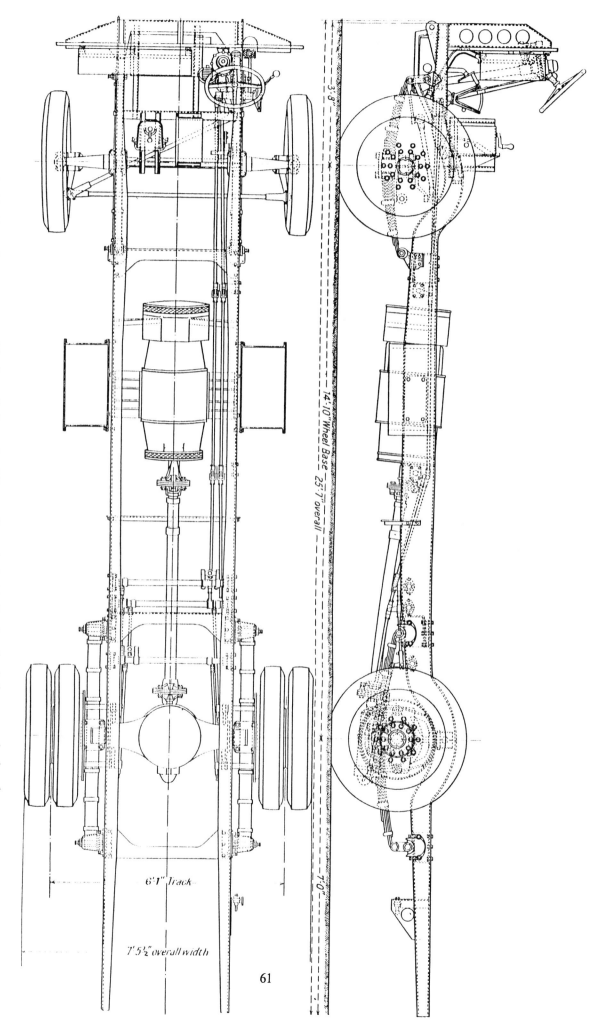

Fig. 74. *General arrangement of the (so-called) standard Garrett four-wheeled trolley bus, braked on rear wheels only, but with the Bull eddy brake on the leading end of the motor.*

6'1" Track

7'5½" overall width

3' 8"

14'10" Wheel Base

25' 7" overall

7' 0"

61

themselves and the costings were all discarded so that there are no details left of how these ventures fared, though from the surviving commercial records we know that no orders resulted.

The production of buses, having got over some teething troubles, might have been thought to have had a reasonable chance of success. The reality, however, was different. A very high proportion of the components came from outside suppliers. Admittedly one of these, Bull Motors Ltd., was a fellow member of the AGE group but under the curious system of accounting practised each constituent had to maximise its earnings, even at the expense of a fellow member, so that Leiston Works was accorded no financial benefit nor, so far as one can tell, any merit marks for trading with Bull Motors. Competition in the limited market for trolley buses was intense so that the margin for profits and overheads was restricted. The position apropos bus production was made worse when it was announced that future AEC production would provide a floor line and, consequently, a rear step level six inches lower than that of the Garrett. Other makers, however reluctantly, had to match this advance. Garretts' financial position simply did not permit them to continue and they withdrew from the market.

Prospective purchasers had been offered a choice of either single or twin motors. The single motors used as standard were 50 nominal horse-power in the four-wheelers and 60 HP in the six-wheelers. The alternative was to fit two 35 HP motors or two 40 HP motors. All of the motors were 500/550 volts series wound. The motors were fitted amidships with prop-shaft drive. On the four-wheelers both the front and rear flexible couplings of the prop-shaft were Hardy disc type, relieved of the weight of the shaft by spherical bearings. The same arrangement was used for the front joint on the six-wheelers but at the rear end of the main prop-shaft and at both ends of the short coupling shaft Hooke type mechanical universal couplings were used. These shafts ran in Ransome & Marles ball bearings.

The electrical control equipment used was provided by The British Thomson-Houston Co.Ltd. of Rugby, though in its sales literature the firm offered to supply equipment by other manufacturers if specifically requested to do so, but in practice this did not happen. A foot-operated master controller carrying auxiliary currents only controlled panel mounted traction type contactors with a separate hand-operated reversing controller. None of this, of course, was unique to Garretts.

Other proprietary components used in the buses included Timken roller bearings, David Brown rear axles, worms and worm wheels and, after the initial dalliance with solid tyres, Dunlop steel disc wheels carrying 40" x 8" tyres. The rear wheels of the four-wheelers were twins but the six-wheelers had single wheels throughout. The front axle was of modified centre point steering type with the worm and worm wheel steering gear inside the driver's cab, all running in ball bearings and connected to the track rods by means of an enclosed vertical shaft. The front axle bed itself was a 40 ton tensile steel stamping of I-section from Kirkstall. The pivots worked in bronze bushes with ball thrust bearings to transmit the weight. The 'S'-type and the earlier 'O'-types were braked on the rear wheels only but subsequently, as already remarked, four-wheeled brakes were fitted in many cases. Probably the most advanced braking was on the Holland demonstrator. Beside being braked on all wheels this had braking that, in a number of further respects, was more advanced than that on the so-called standard four-wheeler. The foot pedal worked the front and one set of rear wheel brakes, the other rear set being actuated by the hand brake lever. Besides this the bus was fitted with a Reavall motor driven compressor and air brakes acting on the same shoes as the foot brake. This system, too, was controlled by a foot pedal. Additionally it had the Bull eddy current system fitted. This was described by the makers in the following words:

THE ADVANTAGES OF THE EDDY CURRENT BRAKE.
1. It will reduce to a minimum the heavy expenditure necessitated by refitting brake linings of friction brakes at frequent intervals.
2. It is smooth in operation and does not possess any of the snatchiness which is to be found in Rheostatic braking and Regenerative control. These are liable to impose very high voltages upon the motor if applied suddenly when the vehicle is travelling at high speed, and there is also the risk of damage to the lamps in the case of Regenerative control.
3. It does not impose extra duty on the motor.
4. There is no frictional contact and no wearing part, therefore the maintenance may be taken as negligible.
5. It can be used down to a very low speed. On a recent test it was found that a bus fully loaded could be brought down a steep hill and the speed could be regulated **by use of the Eddy Current Brake down to about 4 m.p.h.**

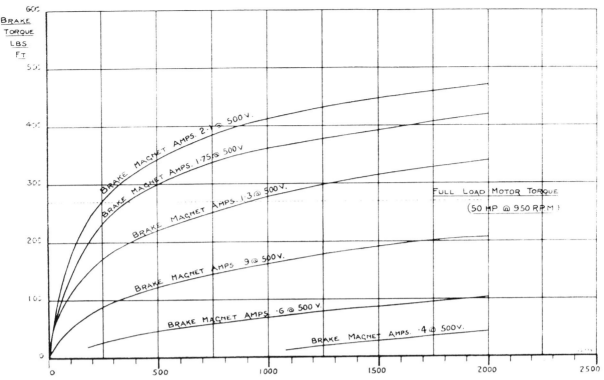

Performance curve of "The Bull Patent Eddy Current Brake."

PERFORMANCE.

The performance of the brake is shown on the curve on the accompanying diagram which gives six different intensities of magnetisation.

Taking the top curve which shows the brake fully applied, the energy required to magnetise being 1 K.W. at 500 volts, it will be seen that the maximum braking effort obtained at 2 000 r.p.m., which corresponds to about 27 m.p.h., is 470 lbs. feet. As the vehicle slows down, the braking power falls off very slowly until a speed of about 250 r.p.m. corresponding to about 3½ m.p.h. is reached. At this point the braking torque available is 270 lbs. feet torque which is equal to the full load torque of the standard 50 H.P. Bull Motor. It will be evident that a very considerable torque is available, even at low speeds. At speeds below 250 r.p.m. on the motor, the braking torque falls off rapidly to nil when the vehicle is at a standstill. It will thus be seen that in the majority of cases **it is possible to control the vehicle and attain adequate deceleration at all speeds down to 3 m.p.h. by use of the Eddy Current Brake alone.**

The energy to be absorbed varies as the square of the speed from which the vehicle is brought to rest. If we assume a low speed of 20 m.p.h. as the average speed at which the brakes are applied and also assume that the Eddy Current Brake will be used down to 3 m.p.h., the friction brakes will be relieved of between 97 and 98% of the duty and consequent wear which they would sustain if used alone. **In other words, the life of the friction brake linings would be increased somewhat about forty times the average figure at present obtained.**

CONSTRUCTION.

The principle involved is the mounting of a specially designed and short-circuited steel rotor on the end of the motor shaft. This rotor is embraced by a special design of magnetic field frame in such a manner that the rotor revolves in the direct path of the magnetic flux when the field magnets are excited. There is a permanent air gap of about $1/10''$ between the rotor and the field frame and no frictional contact of any sort is permitted. **The braking effect is simply that produced by the short circuited rotor revolving within the magnetic field and is caused by the short circuit current set up within the rotor itself.** The braking power is dissipated entirely within the cast steel rotor in the form of heat. The rotor is fitted with a number of heat radiating fins and air is drawn through by means of a powerful fan fitted on the end of the shaft. By this means, it is possible to keep the rotor down to a safe working temperature.

METHOD OF OPERATION.

The method employed in operating the brake is to apply current to the field windings of the magnet frame by means of a graduated controller operated by a foot pedal. The braking torque obtained varies with the speed and also with the intensity of the current following through the magnet windings.

APPLICATION.

In cases where the Eddy Current Brake is ordered, our standard practice is to arrange **to operate this brake and the foot friction brake by the same pedal,** the first portion of the travel bringing the Eddy Current Brake fully on, and the second portion applying the friction brake while holding the Eddy Current Brake full on. Thus in the case of a trolley leaving the line while the Eddy Current Brake is in operation, all the driver need do to effect an emergency stop is to depress the foot pedal fully, thus obtaining the full effect of his friction brake, and if necessary apply the hand brake in addition.

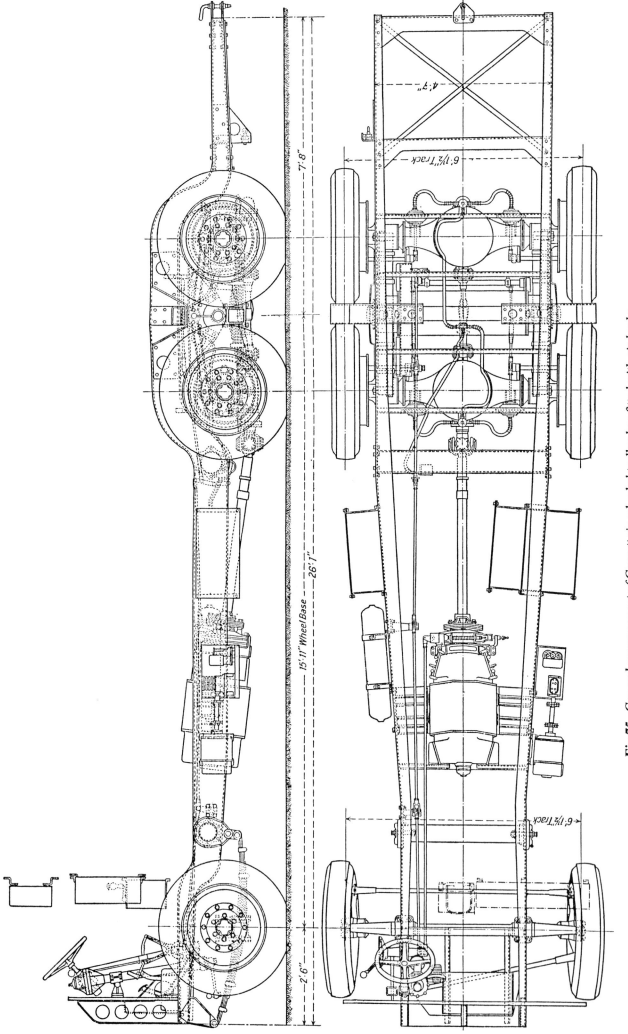

Fig. 75. *General arrangement of Garrett six-wheeled trolley bus fitted with air brake.*

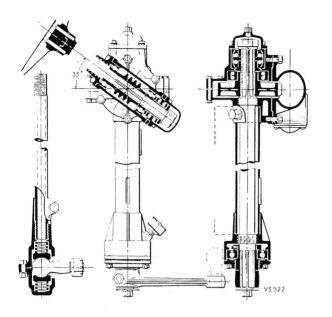

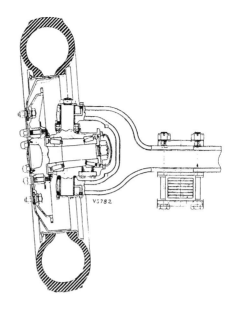

Fig.76. *Sectional view of the steering gear of a Garrett trolley bus.*

Fig.77. *Cross section of the front axle showing the roller bearing and ball thrust bearing.*

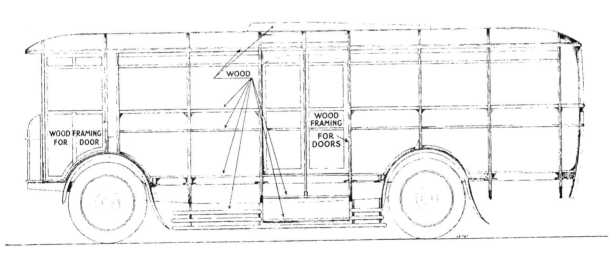

WOOD

WOOD FRAMING FOR DOOR

WOOD FRAMING FOR DOORS

Figs.78. (above) and 79. (right) *show how the composite body framing of a Garrett single decker, as built at Leiston Works, was arranged. No doubt the bodies from Roe and Strachan & Brown were similar.*

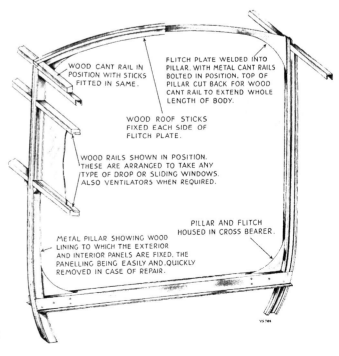

WOOD CANT RAIL IN POSITION WITH STICKS FITTED IN SAME.

FLITCH PLATE WELDED INTO PILLAR. WITH METAL CANT RAILS BOLTED IN POSITION, TOP OF PILLAR CUT BACK FOR WOOD CANT RAIL TO EXTEND WHOLE LENGTH OF BODY.

WOOD ROOF STICKS FIXED EACH SIDE OF FLITCH PLATE.

WOOD RAILS SHOWN IN POSITION. THESE ARE ARRANGED TO TAKE ANY TYPE OF DROP OR SLIDING WINDOWS. ALSO VENTILATORS WHEN REQUIRED.

PILLAR AND FLITCH HOUSED IN CROSS BEARER.

METAL PILLAR SHOWING WOOD LINING TO WHICH THE EXTERIOR AND INTERIOR PANELS ARE FIXED. THE PANELLING BEING EASILY AND QUICKLY REMOVED IN CASE OF REPAIR.

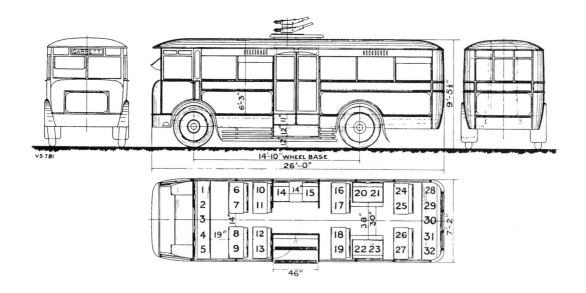

Fig.80. *Plan and elevation of the final single deckers built at Leiston for Mexborough & Swinton.*

Fig.81. *View in Station Works, Spring, 1928, showing (right) No.392, the left-hand drive continental demonstrator, later converted to right-hand control and sold to Ipswich, where it was noted for its heavy steering, so much so that during the second war many of the women drivers found it too tiring to handle. Next to it is Mexborough & Swinton No.40 (Works No.393) and the remaining cars (394-398) of the batch of six then in hand.*

The 'S'-type and, it is believed, some of the earlier 'O'-type trolley buses were fitted with trolley bases of Estler Bros. manufacture, though there is a note from Maurice Plane to his colleague Evans in the buying department (dated April 24, 1924): 'Please order from Peckham Truck & Engineering Co. Ltd. 1 set of collectors comprising 2 railless trolley standards and 2 taped and insulated trolley arms...', but in all of the later vehicles both bases and heads were made at Leiston.

The bodies fitted to the earlier buses, coming as they did from two separate sources, were likely to have contained a considerable amount of their respective manufacturers' standard practices. In the case of the bodies built at Leiston, which, in general principles, resembled those supplied by the sub-contractors, the main transverse body frames were predominantly of steel. Steel cross bearers that rested on the chassis had the pillars housed in each end with a metal gusset plate at the joint. Ash liners were fitted into the pillars to receive the fixings of the exterior panels and body lining. The roof member of each frame was a steel flitch plate with ash roof sticks either side, the roof flitches being welded in, though the metal cant rail that joined the heads of the frames was bolted on, so as to allow removal of an individual frame should it become damaged. An ash cant rail, continuous from end to end, was superimposed upon the metal rail. Intermediate roof sticks, the horizontal body rails below the cant rails, and all other body members were also of ash. The domed roof ends were pressed out of sheet steel. The main section of the roof between them was covered with tongued and grooved and vee-jointed red deal match boarding, and the roofs were weather-proofed with canvas laid in white lead paste. The eaves had a grooved drip rail fixed to the cant rails and drained through a pipe.

External panels and beads were of steel; the interior panels were birch ply, with a fluted aluminium kicker next to the floor. Ceilings were not lined and were painted or stained and varnished as ordered. The window glass was $^3/_{16}$" polished plate glass and the glass to ventilators 21oz. clear sheet glass, both types abominably dangerous in the event of an accident. The edges of the panes were painted with gold size and mounted in rubber strip for water-proofing, and were secured by hardwood fillets fixed with nickel plated cups and screws. The standard external finish applied was a coat of priming, followed by two filler coats, three coats of colour and three coats of varnish, the lettering and lining being put on under the varnish. Of the colours selected by operators Ipswich chose a brightish mid-green, with cream to the lower panels and above waist level. West Hartlepool and Southend each had a basically similar livery but with somewhat darker green. Grimsby and Doncaster chose something approximating to a Midland red. Mexborough & Swinton also used a deep red but without the cream lower panels. Lima selected white and Copenhagen a reddish brown. In the case of Mexborough & Swinton cars the colour used is recorded as Nobles & Hoare Ltd's 'Car Red' over two coats of 'Car Red' undercoat, two of 'Orange Lead Ready Bound', and two of filler, the whole finished with the customary three coats of varnish.

Interior finish varied from operator to operator. The elaborate internal ceiling finish of the Lima cars has already been noticed, but those for use in England had more mundane finishes though the information now in my possession does not enable me to say how each was turned out. The plywood body linings were offered in either varnished finish or with leather cloth to match the backs of the seats. Certain cars such as, for example, the Southend double-deckers, are known to have had seats upholstered in chequered moquette, but generally speaking it is not known conclusively which cars had leather seats and which moquette. The bodies built at Leiston had seats variously by G.D.Peters & Co. Ltd., Siddall & Hilton, or Lace Well. Guard rails, commode handles, budget locks, hinges, interior lights, and most other ironmongery came from Cooper, Webb, Jones, supplemented by a few items from George Johnstone. In cases where bodies were supplied by outside builders they doubtless had their own regular suppliers for such material. The finish used for many commode rails, grab rails and the like was Doverite, made and applied by Doverite Ltd. at Northampton, but some, mostly for Ipswich, had them in polished brass.

Road testing of completed chassis presented a serious problem and one, moreover, that was shared by Ransomes, Sims & Jefferies since neither firm was trading on a scale that would have justified building a private test track with overhead. Both solved their dilemma in the same way, namely, by applying to Ipswich Corporation for permission to use the town's overhead for test runs. At a meeting of the Electricity Supply & Tramways Committee on August 26, 1926, the manager was authorised to allow each of the firms access to the overhead, subject to payment for the current consumed, and to the tests being carried out at such times and over such parts of the routes as the manager might stipulate. Arthur Pipe's recollection of testing Garrett vehicles was that they were towed to Ipswich by whatever steam wagon was available and tested during the small hours - a chilly business for the tester, seated on a bare chassis on a winter night. It was also his recollection that chassis destined to be bodied by Strachan & Brown were towed to their London works, also by steam wagon and also at night. Chassis destined for the Roe works at Leeds were, it is understood, sent by rail as towing that distance would have been too onerous an undertaking.

Within a few months of the start of operations the solid rubber tyres fitted to the Ipswich trolley buses proved to be a mistake. Although speed for speed the buses were quieter than the trams they had replaced, in the matter of vibration the situation was not much improved as they could, and often did, run at speeds in excess of 20 m.p.h., far faster than the trams, which resulted in unacceptable vibration in premises fronting onto the route. The manager seems to have come quickly to the conclusion that the only lasting cure lay in the fitting of pneumatic tyres and had obtained estimates for carrying out the work of conversion from both Garretts and Ransomes, Sims & Jefferies. The working papers of the Garrett estimate are dated May, 1927, and the price came to £128.0s.0d. This was presented to the Committee at its meeting on June 30, 1927. Ransomes wanted rather more (£234. 0s.0d.) and the Committee members were not over pleased at the contemplation of this level of expenditure on alterations to vehicles after less than a year of running. Because of the continuing complaints, at the Committee meeting of July 28, 1927, a speed limit of 12 m.p.h. (i.e. the legal limit) was instituted in Spring Road and Norwich Road. When the Committee again met on September 29, the amelioration resulting from the speed restriction was discussed, and upon its being deemed insufficient, it was decided, as an interim measure, to have one Garrett bus converted to pneumatics, a task finished early in November. Encouraged by the result and by Garretts having agreed to drop the conversion price to £120, the Committee sanctioned the fitting of pneumatics to the whole fleet, a task carried out in stages, a few at a time.

The Ipswich trolley buses were unusual, particularly for municipal undertakings at that time, in having both front and rear doors, and in being equipped for one man operation at times of scant traffic, in practice on Sundays. During such use the rear steps were retracted and the rear doors fixed shut. One man working was much used by the small independent operators and by some of the major undertakings on minor routes but was rare in towns. Ipswich had good service from its Garretts. Five survived the war, and of these No.29 was the last to be withdrawn in 1949. Its chassis is preserved at the Long Shop Museum in Leiston. The body and chassis of No.26, without motor or electrical gear, was salvaged by the Long Shop and kept there until transferred to the Ipswich Transport Museum in Summer, 1995. Much restoration is needed, however. Other Garrett trolley buses did not have such long lives. Those supplied to Bradford were taken out of service in 1937, and the four St.Helens buses the next year. The Mexborough & Swinton cars, however, went on rather longer, and the last was not withdrawn until 1950. One example, fleet No.34, was sold for use as a farm shed and is now in the Sandtoft Transport Centre not far from Doncaster where restoration to working order has not been ruled out in the long term. The only Garrett trolley bus in working order is No.310, No.5 in the Nordsjøellands fleet in Denmark, which was repatriated after being withdrawn from service and is now preserved at the East Anglia Transport Museum, Carlton Colville, Lowestoft.

Quite early in the period during which Leiston Works built trolley buses Harry Keys suggested that the 'O'-type four-wheeler chassis could be used as the basis of a petrol engined bus. He was, however, unable to arouse any boardroom enthusiasm for this suggestion although, as noted in Part 2, outline designs were prepared for both four and six-wheeled *steam* buses. By mid-summer, 1928, when there seemed to be a large and growing fashion amongst passenger transport undertakings for six-wheeled chassis, he thought he might re-open the question. On a visit to the Works in July, 1928, when he attended a meeting at which two directors, Leggett and Bennett, and Garvie, the general manager, were present he put forward the suggestion, backed up by a reasoned case, that an OS chassis should be adapted to receive and be fitted with a 60/70 HP proprietary petrol engine and gear box. He had put in some homework on the idea by discussing with Bull Motors the possibility of using their eddy brake, taking the necessary current from a lighting/starter battery of, as he later put in a confirming memorandum of July 30, 'fairly high capacity'. He went on to add 'If it is possible to incorporate this particular brake on a petrol driven chassis undoubtedly this machine would be one of the finest petrol vehicles on the market.' With typical defeatism, Bennett jotted his thoughts on the foot of the memo :

1]   Design   2]   Development   3]   Estimate of cost compared with current competing types

4]   How much to lay out?   Engine: Gearbox: Radiator: Lighting + starting set + battery: E.C.Brakes

Clearly not encouraged by his conclusions on the likely costs, by way of reply Bennett temporised, saying merely that he would give the idea careful consideration. He asked Keys whom he had in mind as suppliers of the 'bought-in' components; what clients were having to pay to other manufacturers for similar buses; and what potential clients thought of the suggestion. Within a couple of days Keys was back with an answer. Potts, the Doncaster general manager, was of the opinion 'that there was a very fine market for a proposition of this kind'. Potts apparently had commented that there were but few six-wheeled chassis on offer and that of those offered only one was really worth looking at. The engine-makers Keys suggested as possibles were Dorman, Astor, White & Poppe, and Continental, advising the choice of an English engine for preference. When referring to White & Poppe I think he was confusing them, who had by then been taken over by Dennis, with E.H. White who made, or marketed, various sizes of petrol engines. As to the rest of the components he wrote, with some asperity, perhaps sensing that he was being fobbed off, that he 'would suggest that you write round to several of the manufacturers of these components and ascertain the prices and weights'. Nothing more came of the proposal except that Bennett went to the trouble of obtaining a copy of Alfred Alcock's patent (No.291677 of 1928) for putting a novel arrangement of front end staircase into a double-decker.

Had he realised it Keys was fighting for a lost cause. The finances of the firm had become so bad and the viability of the bus work so marginal that it was soon to be abandoned altogether, but nevertheless he persevered in his efforts. Almost his last endeavour for the firm was to secure the details of a projected trolley bus route from Saronno to Cuggiono, about 25 kilometres, on the outer fringes of the Milan conurbation in Italy. He succeeded in establishing contact with Fogliani, the Milan transport manager, but it went no further. How it was intended to deal with the manufacture of buses for the Saronno project had the contract been secured is not known with certainty, but some light is thrown upon it by a document discovered when the old strong-room at the Town Works was cleared of its contents in the 70's. This was the draft, dated December 1, 1930, of an agreement with Ansaldo of Turin to grant the right to build Garrett trolley buses for use in Italy. Ansaldo already had a licence to build the Garrett three-shaft roller based upon the 4CD tractor design. Victor Garrett negotiated the deal with Graziani & Co. Ltd., Ansaldo's London agents, having been in intermittent contact with them since 1927. The text of the agreement is given below. It is of interest to note what trivial sums, by today's standards, Garretts stood to gain by the arrangement!

AN AGREEMENT made this the _____ day of _____ One thousand nine hundred and thirty_____ between Richard Garrett & Sons, Limited, whose registered office is at Leiston Works, Leiston, England (hereinafter called "the Company") of the one part and _____ _____ whose head office is situate at _____ (hereinafter called "the Licensee") of the other part WHEREAS the Company have manufactured a large number of Electric Trolley Buses and have agreed with the Licensees to grant unto the Licensees to the extent and upon the terms hereinafter expressed and contained a Licence to make use exercise and vend Electric Trolley Buses according to the designs of the Company NOW THIS AGREEMENT WITNESSETH and it is hereby mutually agreed and declared as follows:-

1.   In consideration of the payments hereinafter reserved and of the agreements on the part of the Licensees hereinafter contained the Company hereby grant unto the Licensees licence and authority in the territory hereinafter mentioned to make Electric Trolley Buses but excluding the electric motors therefor according to the designs of the Company and to use exercise and vend Electric Trolley Buses manufactured according to such designs.

2.   During the continuance of this Licence the Company shall not in the said territory make Electric Trolley Buses to the designs of the Company nor shall the Company within the said territory use exercise and vend Electric Trolley Buses manufactured according to such designs.

3.   The said territory shall be the area comprised within the boundaries of the Kingdom of Italy.

4.   In consideration of the Licence hereby granted and of the agreements on the part of the Company herein contained:

[a]   On the signing of these presents the Licensees shall pay to the company the sum of Two hundred and fifty pounds sterling.

[b]   The Licensees shall also pay to the Company a further sum of Two hundred and fifty pounds sterling as follows:

[i]   Fifty pounds sterling so soon as the Licensees shall have manufactured the first five Electric Trolley Buses whether made to the Company's designs or not and whether as chassis only or completed buses.

[ii]   Fifty pounds sterling so soon as each further five Electric Trolley Buses as aforesaid shall have been manufactured, but so that the sum of the amounts paid to the Company by the Licensees in respect of these further payments shall at the end of eighteen months from the date of this agreement be not less than One hundred and twenty five pounds sterling and at the end of three years from the date of this agreement not less than Two hundred and fifty pounds sterling whether in either case the requisite number of Buses shall have been manufactured or not.

5.   The Licensees shall at their office at _____ _____ keep true and particular accounts of all matters relating to the manufacture of Electric Trolley Buses by them and will on every Thirty first day of March Thirtieth day of June Thirtieth day of September and Thirty first day of December render to the

Company a true and particular account of all Electric Trolley Buses manufactured by them, whether the same be manufactured according to the designs of the Company or not during the preceding three calendar months. The Company shall be entitled by themselves or their agent or agents in writing by them appointed at all reasonable times (not exceeding once during any consecutive three calendar months) to inspect and take copies of or extracts from any books accounts or documents in the possession or under the control of the Licensees and relating in whole or in part to the manufacture of Electric Trolley Buses by the Licensees.

6.   The Company shall supply to the Licensees one complete set of working drawings specifications and manufacturing data relating to each type of the Company's standard designs of Electric Trolley Buses but excluding the electric motors therefor.

7.   The Licensees shall be at liberty to send a representative or representatives to the Works of the Company to the intent that such representative or representatives may gain such information and experience as may be necessary to enable the Licensees to manufacture the Company's designs of Electric Trolley Buses to the best advantage. All expenses relating to the sending to and from and maintenance in England of such representative or representatives shall be borne and paid by the Licensees.

8.   The Licensees shall not assign transfer sublet mortgage charge or part with this licence or any part thereof to any person or persons or Company whomsoever without the previous consent in writing of the Company.

9.   Any notice hereunder may be served by prepaid registered letter sent through the post to the Company at their Leiston Works Leiston aforesaid or to the Licensees at _____.

10.   The Licensees shall forthwith procure the execution by a Bank to be approved by the Company of an instrument in writing (in a form to be mutually agreed between the Company and the said Bank) guaranteeing the due payment of all moneys at any time to become due or payable to the Company under the terms of this Licence.

11.   All stamp duties on this Licence and Agreement shall be borne and paid by the Licensees.

12.   The Company shall in no wise be liable to indemnify the Licensees in respect of any actions proceedings demands claims costs damages or expenses taken or made against or paid by the Licensees in relation to any infringement by them of any patent rights in the said territory possessed by third parties and relating to Electric Trolley Buses or any part or parts thereof.

13.   If any disputes difficulties or questions shall arise between the parties hereto (or between the Company and any permitted assignees of the Licensees) with respect to their rights or liabilities or otherwise under these presents or to the meaning or construction thereof the same shall be referred to the decision of a Single Arbitrator who shall be appointed by the President of the Institution of Mechanical Engineers and shall sit in London and this shall be deemed a submission to Arbitration within the Arbitration Act 1889 or any Statutory modification or re-enactment thereof for the time being in force the provisions whereof shall apply as far as applicable.

14.   This Licence and Agreement is to be construed and take effect as a Licence and Agreement made in England and in accordance with English Law and the Licensees hereby submit to the jurisdiction of the High Court of Justice in England ------------

IN WITNESS whereof the Company have caused their Common Seal to be hereunto affixed and _____ _____ has hereunto set his hand for and behalf of the Licensees the day and year first above written.

Although Ansaldo subsequently built trolley buses I have no evidence that Garrett designs were used in any of them.

Setting trolley buses to work could give rise to problems as it had with the undertype steam wagons. So far as I am aware, the service inspectors appointed primarily to deal with steam wagon customers had no contact with operators of trolley buses, but just as Arthur Pipe had fulfilled the function of 'flying fitter' in respect of steam wagons so H.J.Woolnough was selected to do the same for buses. Correspondingly where J.K.Peecock had frequently provided the administration presence to deal with disgruntled customers and their complaints, it was often Bill Deane who was sent to smooth ruffled feathers arising from trolley bus matters. Setting buses to work at Ipswich or Southend and coping with any resultant problems could be dealt with relatively easily by sending out personnel direct from the Works, but settling those sold further north required staff to be based nearer at hand. For some time during 1928 Woolnough stayed in lodgings in Hamelyn Road, Conisborough, within easy reach of the Mexborough & Swinton cars, and not too distant from St.Helens, Doncaster, and Grimsby. Some of the problems that arose were trivial in their cause but tiresome in their effect. One of the Doncaster six-wheelers, for instance, developed a short circuit which was found to have been caused by a screw in the cable trough having pricked a lighting lead. At the end of March, 1928, there was a problem at the Mexborough & Swinton as Woolnough reported on March 26:

I had to work all Friday night as three of the buses were alive; on each bus the fault was on the headlights section.

He also found excessive movement in the steering heads of cars Nos.34 and 35 (Works Nos.379 and 380) where the holes in the casting turned out to be oversize, a fault which, by implication at least, he attributed to careless fitting at the Works. Successive reductions in the numbers employed and cutting of piece rates had led to a degree of demoralisation among the Leiston fitters, as already noted in connection with undertype steam wagons.

Again, when he was setting cars 38 and 39 (Works Nos.383 and 384) to work on March 25, he found that the trolley base springs on 38 were so weak that if screwed up sufficiently to give the right tension on the overhead they were completely closed up when the trolley arms were down, thus removing any chance of putting more tension on later if so required after a period in service. The offside front spring on 39 was weak under load so that with a full complement on the car the tyre was liable to rub on the wing. This batch of six buses (Works Nos.379 to 384 - fleet Nos.34 to 39) seem to have had more than their share of problems. The spring ends were found to be a bad fit in the cast steel brackets - all of which came from John Brown & Sons of Sheffield - up to ¼" of side play being found in the worst case, and William McGibbon, the Mexborough general manager, considered there was too much play and, hence, excessive rattles in the brakes, both in the rigging and on the shoes within the drums. He also reckoned that the headlamp brackets were of a faulty design and that a swan-neck inlet was needed at the back of the lamp to prevent the entry of water and consequent shorting. Furthermore, he complained, movement in the bodies was already resulting in cracking of the paint below the windows and serious leakage was occurring between the windscreen and the dash causing several trolley indicator lamps to burn out. More surprisingly he complained that the rear wheels stood out a little beyond the mudguards. Not only did this lead to splashing of the panels but it infringed the Ministry of Transport regulations on vehicle width as did the top ventilator windows in that, having no stops, they could be opened beyond the body-line. McGibbon emphasised that all the defects needed to be put right promptly as it was the intention to order further buses in April, 1928, and that would not be implemented until the current batch was satisfactory. Once more the faithful Bill Deane was sent to remedy and pacify. What needed to be done to rectify the body and width problems was not recorded, but John Brown & Sons were told to remedy the spring defects and, by the supply of a quantity of spares from the Works, Woolnough was able to deal with the brakes and other chassis troubles.

The percentage of the home market in trolley buses attributable to Garretts during the period 1925-30 was far more substantial than is sometimes supposed. Guy of Wolverhampton led the field with 25.5% but Garretts, with 20%, were close behind, followed by English Electric (13%), and Ransomes (10.5%). Railless, despite their pioneer work, supplied only 5%, Straker Clough 6%, and Straker Squire 5%, the latter figure just exceeded by Tilling Stevens (5.5%) but not by Karrier (4%) or by the combined efforts of ADC and AEC (4%). Leyland contributed a mere 1.5%. An analysis of the succeeding decade would have shown a radically differing result, but in their time Garretts were far from negligible.

Rear view of Garrett Rigid Six Wheeler chassis.

71

Fig.82. No.387, the first Garrett six-wheeler, in Station Works complete but unpainted. Originally put in hand as a speculation in February, 1927, as a single decker, it was changed subsequently to double deck and eventually sold to Southend-on-Sea on February 28, 1929, having been in the meantime to various shows and on hire to Southend. [S.R.O.]

Fig.83. The first order for Garrett double deckers consisted of the four (385, 386, 388, and 389) for Doncaster delivered between January and April, 1928, fitted with Roe bodies. This is No.385.

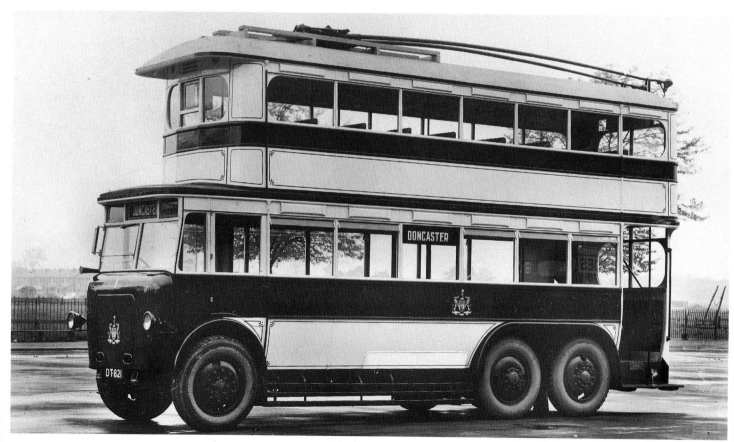

Fig.84. *Rear end view of No.385 showing the twin trolley pole mountings. It is not clear whether these were adopted to be uniform with the Karriers with which they were to work or to give a reduction in overall height, probably the latter as the Southend cars had the same type of bases.*

Fig.85. *The five further cars for Southend (Works Nos.414-418 inc), delivered May to July, 1929, all had enclosed staircases. The plan and elevations are shown below.*

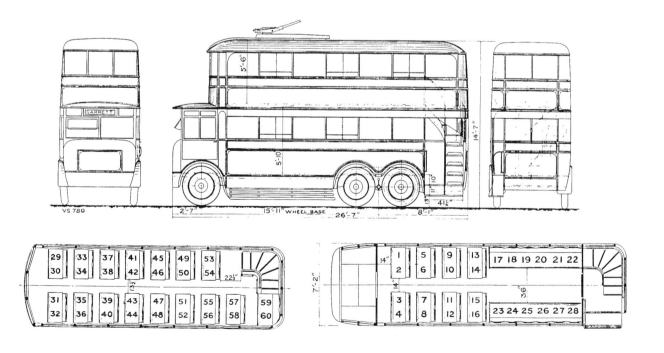

Fig.86. Southend No.105 (Works No.414) embarking passengers for Prittlewell in the town centre. The high loading line is painfully evident.

Fig.87. Interior of the lower deck of No.105. Most of the buses supplied by Garretts had leather covered seating. Southend, by contrast chose moquette.

Fig.88. The upper deck of Southend-on-Sea's No.105.

Fig.89. A posed line-up of Mexborough & Swinton cars headed by No.38 (Works No.380), fitted with twin trolley bases, whereas earlier cars (such as No.34) had had the superimposed type.

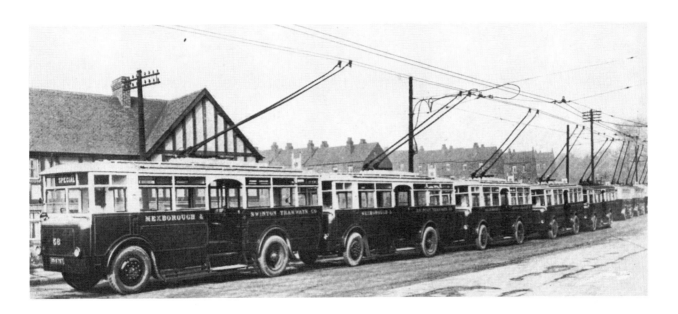

Fig.90. No.324 was the initial GTZ which was tested by Glasgow Corporation in February, 1927, and accepted as fully satisfactory. The only major alterations made to it were the substitution of a more conventional shape of cab, as shown on the production series below, and amendment to the body front. [S.R.O.]

Fig.91. The scene at the Top Works in February, 1928, showing eighteen GTZs waiting to be loaded onto rail for shipment to Glasgow, with the Works power-house and chimney in the background.

Fig.92. The scene outside the Govan garage as the destructor plant was opened by H.R.H. Prince George in April, 1928.

Chapter 5

The Glasgow GTZ

Even before the 1914-18 War the Glasgow city authorities - both elected members and their officers - had been dissatisfied with the methods of refuse collection in the city areas south of the Clyde. Indeed a committee had been set up as early as 1912 to investigate the problems of the area and to suggest courses of action but the War had led to the initiatives being abandoned. The members of a second committee which was appointed in the twenties to re-examine the situation as it then existed visited disposal works in some of the major cities of Europe. As a result of their studies they formulated a report which advised the Corporation to set up a processing plant to screen out metals from the refuse, to crush and burn the residue in a power-station fuelled solely on refuse, and to utilise the resultant clinker as an aggregate for making concrete flags and curbs.

These proposals were adopted virtually as presented and the resultant plant - the largest of its type in Europe - was constructed on a difficult site at Craigton Road, Govan. It was designed as a model for its purpose, making use of mechanical means as far as possible for handling the refuse and giving an output of 10 000 kilowatts. Concurrently with the contract for the construction of this disposal plant the Corporation set in hand an investigation of means whereby it might improve and mechanise the methods of domestic refuse collection. The direction of this part of the reorganisation was put in the hands of Mr. W.Greig, the Cleansing Superintendent, and deputed by him in turn to his lieutenant, Colin McFarlane. Because refuse collection in this largely tenement area of Glasgow was done mostly at night McFarlane decided early in the project that his new vehicles were to be electric both for silence of operation and for ease of slow movement control as well as for the essential economy of using current generated from the burned refuse, but although the Corporation already ran a fleet of twenty-two electric vehicles including two Garrett 2½ ton end tippers, none fulfilled the postulates he had formulated.

Firstly he wanted a loading line no higher than 4' 6" to 4' 9". Secondly he required his vehicles to carry 14 cubic yards of refuse, the weight of which would vary between perhaps 4½ and 6½ tons according to area and time of year, most of which was to be carried below the loading line, and, thirdly, he required good performance characteristics - a turning circle of fifty feet or less, a loaded speed of 12 m.p.h. when running to the disposal plant from the last pick-up, and the ability to run 40 miles between charges. In addition the bodies were to be side tippers. No electric vehicle designs then on offer came anywhere near McFarlane's stipulations but he was determined not to abate them nor to fall into line with what the manufacturing firms wished to impose, believing, correctly as it turned out, that it was possible to achieve a design compatible with the improved work practices which he wished to institute. For this reason the requirements were made the basis of the conditions under which tenders were invited for the thirty-six vehicles required. McFarlane calculated that the potential order, which would amount to close on £40 000, would attract considerable interest amongst manufacturers and stimulate the production of suitable designs of vehicle. Justifiable though his belief appeared to be, it proved not to be correct.

Jack Simpson, as related in Parts 1 and 2, had become involved in the selling of electric vehicles more or less by accident. In February, 1926, he was sent for by Col. Garrett who outlined to him the onerous conditions attached to the Glasgow invitation to tender. 'I believe', he remarked to Jack, 'that we can get an order here if we handle the matter right. Go to Glasgow, meet McFarlane, and see how it can be done.' Jack arranged to meet McFarlane on the following Friday. He travelled overnight to Glasgow and spent most of the day with him discussing and sizing up the problem, and the whole of the evening drinking with him. McFarlane could see off most men at whisky drinking but did not defeat Jack - perhaps the first step the latter took towards achieving the high esteem in which, ultimately, he came to be held by McFarlane who, never a patient man, had been irritated beyond measure by the defeatism and 'take-it-or-leave-it' attitudes of the representatives of the other makers. Consequently he found Jack's difference of attitude refreshing in that he accepted that the stringent performance specification was a real and practical requirement and not a vague statement of an ideal.

On the Saturday he broke his journey home at his parents-in-law's home in Lancashire where his wife Lilian was on a visit. He borrowed his mother-in-law's pastry board for use as a drawing board and roughed out some ideas as to how the design might be worked out. What he drew convinced him that the specification could be met, albeit with difficulty. His report to Col. Garrett was 'The man knows what he wants, and is determined to have it. It can be done, and no-one else is trying.' His outline of how he proposed to go about it was greeted with scepticism by the two other directors present, Bennett and Leggett whose chronic pessimism had dogged the undertype wagon project, but Jack remained adamant that everything he had suggested was possible if he were to be allowed the full use for three weeks of A.J.Serve's time. Serve, another chronic pessimist, was intensely engaged at that moment on the design of the trolleybuses. His earlier experience with Silvertown and his deep knowledge of electric vehicles, coupled with his capacity for original thought made him an ideal collaborator. At first, in his customary manner, he threw up his hands at the impossibility as he saw it of carrying out the task in the time available, but soon he and Jack were deep in debate as to how the latter's outline schemes, worked out largely on intuition, could be translated into sound vehicle practice.

An early problem was the shape of the battery which was dictated by the space available. Up to that time Garretts had used mainly Chloride batteries but no existing Chloride designs fitted and the makers showed no enthusiasm for producing a special for, in their eyes, such a small order. Jack spent a frustrating day phoning battery makers, none of whom seemed to have any interest in the work he was offering. Probably the word had been put around that the Glasgow requirements were impossible to fulfil and that the whole thing was thus a wild goose chase. Whatever the reason the Garrett bid seemed at the point of being defeated for want of the right battery when someone suggested phoning Tudor, at that time considered a second eleven maker, at Dukinfield. Jack asked them on the phone if they could do batteries in the shape and properties he required. 'Lad' came the enthusiastic response from the other end, 'for that order we can do 'em any shape tha' likes.'

Finally there remained the problem of accommodating tipping gear. Both as to weight, and the space taken up, tipping gear on the vehicle was a nuisance, adding to the unladen weight and hence the power consumption - already a critical point - whilst, at the same time, pushing up the cost per vehicle. It was during a discussion of this that Serve was having with Jack Simpson that the latter had an idea. Since the thirty-six vehicles were to tip into the same four hoppers why go to the trouble and expense of putting tipping gear on each vehicle when eight overhead hoists at the hoppers would be capable of achieving the same objective at a saving both in capital cost and maintenance. On being sounded on the matter McFarlane was enthusiastic. Serve and Simpson completed their design, prepared their estimate and laid it before Col. Garrett. The tender, dated March 3, 1926, for thirty-six vehicles at £1 078. 0s. 0d. each delivered to Glasgow, was submitted and, in a letter of March 24, 1926, accepted. Jack Simpson and Serve were jubilant and Col. Garrett was pleased, but Bennett and Leggett remained sceptical, doubting that the vehicle would satisfy the performance specification as to mileage per charge.

The Spring of 1926 was marred nationally by the coal strike, the brief General Strike, and a further period of the coal strike. In Leiston management circles there was the additional anxiety as to whether or not the new refuse collector would perform in practice as had been predicted in Serve's calculations. During this anxious period Bennett once came up behind Simpson and Serve whilst they were discussing some point concerning the GTZs and remarked to Jack 'I could have covered myself with medals, with orders like that!' Because of his conviction that the venture would fail he was reluctant to put the whole batch in hand. In a letter to the Corporation written on June 22, Garretts suggested they complete one only in advance of the general run - to enable it to undergo site approval trials. This again McFarlane approved. Serve, with aid from Bill Deane, the other Leiston draughtsman engaged mainly upon electric vehicle work, settled down to the slog of detailing.

The prototype became No.324 in the electric vehicle series. Work on it was completed on February 25, 1927, and it was test run over roads around the Works and over the road from Leiston to Aldeburgh. Its supporters had realised that the performance on one battery charge would be a close-run thing but it was a relief when the test runs at Leiston were found to be accomplished just within the stipulations. As a result it was sent off by rail to Glasgow for its acceptance trials with Messrs. Simpson and Serve travelling to meet it. With the thoroughness that had characterised his actions all through the project Jack Simpson took Serve with him on a test run over the actual terrain on which the wagon was to work. Jogging through the daytime traffic on the south side of Glasgow it horrified them by producing a mileage wildly short of the forty specified. Once again Jack's presence of mind did not fail him. They recharged the batteries, waited until late in the evening and then tried it over the sparsely trafficked streets. The result was gratifying - some three miles over the minimum.

Fig. 93. *On a dour day in 1928 a line of loaded GTZs climbs the inclined roadway from Helen Street towards the discharge hoppers of the Govan plant headed by wagon No.23 (Works No.365). The next is No.25 (Works No.367).*

Fig. 94. *At the top of the incline the loaded wagons discharged into hoppers , the bodies being tipped by hoists on overhead runways, supplied by the Glasgow firm of John Deas & Co. The wagons (l. to r.) are Nos.12, 5, and 33 (Works Nos.354, 347, and 375). Despite the works being probably the most modern in Europe and only a year or so old, note the untidiness and physical damage seemingly inseparable from such operations.*

Fig.95. *No.32 (Works No.374) being discharged into the hopper, the picture giving a better view of the hoisting gear and showing how the side doors of the wagons opened.*

Fig.96. *Empty wagons going down the incline towards Craigton Road, with the vehicle garage behind the first wagon.*

The following day he saw Colin McFarlane and put it to him that, as the lorry was for night service, it was only logical and right that the appraisal trial should be carried out at night. McFarlane was no fool and possibly saw through the subterfuge but by that time he liked the vehicle too much to let it fail its tests. At all events - and probably because of his advice - the Corporation agreed to allow the critical approval run to be done at night and, as a result the vehicle acquitted itself with honour. The two Garrett men sent off a triumphant telegram to the Works and retired to their hotel room. Bennett and Leggett, who had been totally convinced that failure could not have been averted, had not waited for the message giving the result, but had travelled up to Glasgow by the night train with the idea, as Jack Simpson put it, 'of seeing what could be salvaged from the fiasco'. Arriving tired and stiff at the hotel they went up to the room occupied by Simpson and Serve to find the pair in bed having celebrated their success with tankards of Guiness and champagne. Far from a day of gloom and repentance as they had expected, the two directors spent the day with Simpson and Serve as guests of honour of the City on a round of visits and inspections culminating in a dinner in the evening.

No.324, finished in dreadnought grey with the Corporation's coat of arms on the offside of the cab, became No.1 in the new fleet destined to work out of Govan Works. Fleet Nos.2 - 36 inclusive bore the consecutive Works Nos. 344 to 378. No.2 was delivered on December 22, 1927, and No.36 on May 16, 1928. Meanwhile the Govan destructor/generating station had been opened by H.R.H. Prince George on April 27, 1928. Because of its large size, almost total mechanisation, and advanced methods, it was much written about in the engineering press, and the actual opening, involving a popular member of the Royal Family, was noted in the national dailies.

The completion of the first batch was followed by a repeat order for six more, Works Nos. 419 to 424. Although 419 was completed first, on June 29, 1929, it took fleet No.42 and No.420 became fleet No.37, the others following in sequence between September 28 and 30, 1929. No.419 was actually delivered last, having been shown in the meantime at the Blackpool Cleansing Conference where it attracted much favourable notice but, disappointingly, no orders. In fact the only GTZ's supplied to a customer other than Glasgow Corporation were two for Paisley Corporation (Works Nos.432 and 434) delivered in September, 1930, which followed after a further batch of four (Nos.428 - 431) built for Glasgow between June and September, 1930. Four more, Nos.435 - 438, for Glasgow followed in July and August, 1931, bringing the Glasgow fleet total to fifty. In these and subsequent vehicles the bodywork design was amended to provide an all-over roof with rubber strip curtains for dust prevention. Early in 1932, as narrated in Parts 1 and 2, Leiston Works was taken over by the debenture holders, and it was not until mid-year that normal trading resumed on a much smaller scale under the new owners, Beyer Peacock & Co. Ltd. Glasgow Corporation were one of the first customers of the new management, and had two further GTZ's (Nos. 439 and 440) in March, 1933. Two more (Nos.441 and 442), the last to be supplied new on solid tyres, were delivered in January, 1934.

Colin McFarlane, who had been promoted to the post of Cleansing Superintendent on April 12, 1928, had taken a look at the method of collecting household refuse with a view to more intensive utilisation of the vehicles used. Advocates of petrol engined units argued that they could be double manned, permitting night use in the congested inner city areas and day use in the suburbs, whereas this could not be done with electrics because of the need to recharge the batteries. For his part McFarlane valued the silence of electrics for night work and, for that matter, the advantage of using current generated from the refuse they collected. Whilst he was pondering on this conundrum the accessibility of the battery stand on the GTZ's suggested either to him or to someone on his staff the idea of putting the batteries into a demountable crate, off-loading them by crane at the end of the night shift, substituting a crate of recharged batteries, and sending the vehicle off for a day's work. The policy began to be implemented in 1934. No.442 was the last made with non-detachable batteries, and Nos.443 - 445 (ordered in the autumn of 1934) designed to comply fully with the 1934 Road Traffic Act, had not only detachable battery crates but also, for the first time, pneumatic tyres, albeit at the expense of an unladen weight of 5 tons 4½ cwt. Originally it had been intended to fit 38" x 8" tyres but difficulties with clearances on the bodywork and reluctance to raise the loading line led in the end to 36" x 8" being used.

These three vehicles had hardly entered service when there were complaints from the drivers about the steering being tiresomely stiff because of the resistance of the tyres upon the road at the comparatively low road speeds employed. McConnell, the supervisor of the Govan garage, suggested that lowered gear ratios in the steerage heads was the answer. His choice was a reduction from 11 to 1 (as supplied) to 15 to

1, but in fact, on the suggestion of Leslie Farrow, a ratio of 13 to 1 was offered and adopted which solved the problem. These modifications were carried through into a further batch of four (Works Nos.446 - 449) supplied in 1936. Change of policy was, however, in the air at the Glasgow Cleansing Department. Arthur Bambrough, the General Manager of Leiston Works, in company with A.R. (Reg) King, his deputy, and, ultimately, his successor, had paid a visit to Colin McFarlane at his office in Glasgow, during which McFarlane had outlined to them his ideas on the department's vehicle requirements for the financial year beginning on June 1, 1936. He had seen, and been impressed by, the Scammell Mechanical Horse and was looking for proposals based upon a five or six wheeled articulated design using a compact tractor unit and a semi-trailer with a load capacity of about 10 cubic yards (3 tons), but he also had ideas for a four wheeled rigid vehicle of about that capacity, roughly equivalent to a scaled down GTZ. At that time the fleet still included a number of old type Edison 3-ton electrics with end tipping bodies which had become life-expired and he was doubtless considering replacements for these, but he also had in contemplation the superseding of the existing horse-drawn vehicles used for collecting street litter.

Garretts dutifully and hopefully prepared general arrangement drawings and estimates for both types of vehicle which Bambrough delivered in person to McFarlane on April 15, 1936. These were not successful, however, and Metropolitan Vickers got the order. Nevertheless, in the Autumn of 1936 Garretts did succeed in selling to Glasgow four further GTZ's which incorporated more drastic revisions of design intended to reduce the unladen weight below the 5 ton limit and thereby to qualify for £25 a year less in Road Fund Tax than the previous batch of four. McFarlane had complained earlier to Bambrough that those excess 4½ cwts. per vehicle were costing him a £100 a year in tax. On his return to Leiston Bambrough had consulted Leslie Farrow who predicted confidently that they could be refined out of the design. He and Ernest Cuthbert, later a director of the firm, examined every component, stripping the weight off pound by pound, and the redesigned vehicle eventually weighed in at a half hundred-weight under the 5 ton limit. Not only was there a saving in Road Fund Tax but also an improvement in the mileage from each battery charge. At the same time the opportunity was taken to incorporate a number of modifications suggested by Glasgow Corporation mostly arising from McConnell's experience of maintaining the earlier vehicles. Visually the most striking part of the re-design was a new cab designed to give a more modern appearance than the old pattern which dated, almost unchanged, from 1927. The new cab had raked windscreen, rounded salient angles and fully glazed doors on both driver's and mate's sides - the old cabs had had a fixed side, latterly with glass, next to the driver, and a waist high door with no glass on the other side. The front axle was improved, Ransome & Marles' roller bearings were fitted on the prop shaft, and, in keeping with the period, trafficators were provided.

As it turned out, these four electrics were the last supplied by Garretts to Glasgow - or, indeed, to any authority - though they supplied replacement bodies for the earlier vehicles, a subject to be returned to later on. Competition for electric sales had become much more effective since their first success in 1926. Electricars Ltd. of Birmingham, who had taken over the Edison electric vehicle business in the United Kingdom, had absorbed Electromobile, of Otley, Yorks, in 1933, and had gone on to become one of the constituents of Associated Electric Vehicle Manufacturers in 1936. Metropolitan Vickers Electrical Co. Ltd. of Trafford Park, Manchester, had commenced building electrics in 1934. Victor Electrics, of Burscough Bridge, near Ormskirk, Lancashire, which began in the 1920's, as the brain-child of a Southport baker, by building electrics on extended Model T Ford chassis were also hankering after Glasgow work, though a vehicle of the Glasgow proportions would have been a special for them, larger than their general production run which ran up to a maximum of some 30 cwt. carrying capacity. All three tendered for vehicles that were similar, though not identical, to the GTZ, and all of the tenders were cheaper than Garretts'. Based upon an order for four, the prices (per vehicle) were:

Electricars	£911
Victor	£1 077
Metrovick	£1 099
Garrett	£1 350

Worse for all four tenderers, however, was the competition from the petrol engined camp. In 1937 Glasgow were able to buy two articulated refuse vehicles consisting of Morris Commercial units and Brockhouse semi-trailers for only £604. 0s. 0d. each.

Fig.97.   Impressed, it would seem , by the success of the GTZs in Glasgow, neighbouring   Paisley ordered two for themselves - Works Nos.432, left, and 434 - arranging for them to discharge at the Govan plant. No more followed so presumably the scheme did not work as hoped.

Fig.98. (right)   By the 1930's changed methods and the steadily increasing bulk to weight ratio of refuse dictated a change to the all-over roof and rubber   strip   curtains, together   with   hinged 'greedy-boards' to raise the level of the sides as the wagon   filled.   Works No.435 was photographed on the Theberton Road, near   Leiston   Station, before delivery.

Fig.99. (below). The same wagon   shown   at   the Govan garage.

Fig.100. By March, 1933, when No.440 (Fleet No.53) was ready for delivery, time was running out for solid tyres, and only two more were supplied in this form.

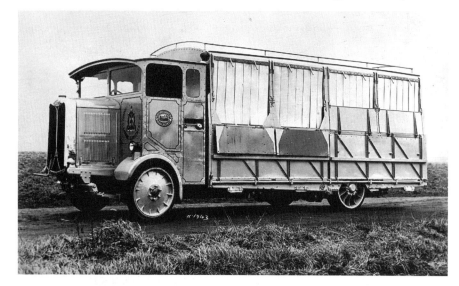

Fig.101. No.35466- the solitary diesel engined GTZ. The high bonnet line was dictated by the engine sub-frame used in it. Whilst the body remained as in the electrics, the front end of the chassis and the form of the cab were altered.

Fig.102. The delay in adopting pneumatics for the GTZ occurred largely because of the problem of accommodating the bulkier rear wheels within the tipping body which Leslie Farrow eventually solved by lateral thinking; i.e. by making a fabricated wheel arch part of the structural body frame. This is Works No.445.

On November 19, 1937, Colin McFarlane was in London with his son and a party of friends and colleagues - Bailie Crawford, Branks (the Glasgow Air Raid Precautions Officer), Catermole of Tudor Accumulators, and a Mr.Collins. Reg King went up to meet them, ostensibly to discuss various points of business, notably some alterations required in eighteen replacement bodies then under construction at the Works. As he put it, in his economical turn of phrase, 'after the usual Friday evening's entertainment' McFarlane professed himself, probably rightly, not in a frame of mind to argue about business that evening, and therefore Reg King met him again at ten o'clock the next morning. Having examined the technical problems of the replacement bodies they turned to the matter which most interested King, namely why Garretts had not received any new orders from Glasgow Corporation. With considerable regret McFarlane explained in great detail, backed up by figures, how the sheer economics of the situation had put Garretts out of the market. The problem was basically insoluble for there was no way in which Garretts, building a batch of about four vehicles, could compete with the mass producers of lorries. Consequently the four GTZs (Nos.450 to 453 inclusive) supplied in 1937 were to be the last road vehicles made by Garretts though they continued to build specialised tractors for off-road use.

In the post-War period of petrol and diesel oil rationing the idea of electric refuse collection vehicles remained attractive to authorities. In February, 1950, Gavin MacArthur, who had succeeded Colin McFarlane as Director of Cleansing in Glasgow, sought tenders for six updated GTZs incorporating, *inter alia*, Lockheed Servo-assisted brakes and a separate cab, behind the driver's compartment, for the loaders. Though the documents were put out as a general invitation to tender, the accompanying specification was framed to incorporate the features of the existing Garrett designs, and it was known that no one other than Garretts would have any interest in it. It is a reflection of the curious state of the country at that time and of the seller's market that existed that Garretts were unable to submit an offer because Bull Motors Ltd. were no longer making suitable traction motors and no other maker could be found to supply a substitute.

The GTZ fleet already at work gave very good service and remained in use, more or less intact, until the latter fifties by which time, despite very thorough general repairs at the Corporation's engineering works at St.Rollox, the effects of twenty-five to thirty years of intensive service were beginning to be apparent. Moreover changes in electricity generation, consequent upon nationalisation, had affected the economics of the Govan destructor generator plant which was approaching the age when its renewal had to be considered. The Corporation decided against renewal, and the works was closed in 1960, removing by its departure one of the financial props of the electric vehicle fleet. The final consideration, however, was the increasing bulk to weight ratio of refuse because of the decline in the use of the domestic grate in which, in earlier years, so much light refuse had been burned and which, in its turn, had contributed a considerable volume of coal cinders to the refuse. This change in refuse characteristics meant that to obtain anything like a full load, in weight terms, compactor vehicles had to be used. Because the GTZs were so highly thought of, the Department considered the possibility of re-equipping them with compactor type bodies to increase the weight of refuse carried to an economic level. Burns, Tudor's engineer/representative in Scotland, maintained close contact with the Glasgow Cleansing Department. Whilst he was in London with Rawson, a Tudor colleague, for the 1958 Electrical Engineers' Exhibition (March 25-29) he took the opportunity to visit Arthur Bambrough, the Leiston General Manager, to brief him on the position, so far as he knew it, concerning the GTZs. Bambrough minuted the salient points gleaned from the meeting:

1] All present Garrett vehicles will be written off and scrapped in the next seven years.
2] The outstanding service given to the Corporation by Garrett Electric Vehicles is so highly appreciated that they wish to have replacements of (Garrett) Electrics.
3] They are as yet unable to find any manufacturer willing to supply Electric Vehicles.
4] They are now fitting 'Gibson' Compactor Bodies to Garrett Vehicles on an enlarged test basis - this is the best of its kind and appears what they are looking for. This body is also being fitted to an Aberdeen Cleansing Vehicle.
   We understand that Gibson body only fitted to Diesel Vehicles to date and that Electric Vehicles as R.G. so fitted would attract attention by other authorities desirous of changing from Diesel and Petrol operated as at Edinburgh. The makers are a small concern only and their capacity is likely to be stretched by increased business in this larger field - present car body and similar panel work.
   Their body also tips and the compactor section assists clearing when end tipping.
5] Combining the above, we believe, and Mr. Burns will probe this whilst indicating, as I believe Glasgow's Mr. Fairlie wished him to ascertain (they being personal friends of many years standing) that we are still interested in possibility of making vehicles.

Although the reaction of the Richard Garrett Engineering Works management to this sounding exercise is believed to have been favourable, no business resulted. Consequently the GTZs were finally phased out until the last unit, fleet No.57 (Works No.445 of 1935) was withdrawn in 1964 , bringing the saga to a close.

The power unit of the GTZ was a 12 HP motor designed for the purpose by Bull Motors Ltd. The frame and brackets were of cast steel, and the armature shaft revolved in ball and roller bearings. Because it was mounted low down between the chassis side members and correspondingly exposed to road dirt and moisture Bull had been requested to give particular attention to the seals and, so far as is known, they were very successful in this respect as no trouble was reported with the motors from first to last. A short prop shaft, with Hooke joints each end, took the drive to an underslung worm on the rear axle assembly which incorporated a four pinion differential. Running voltage for journeys from depot to collecting area and vice versa was 80/85 volts but a change-over switch was provided by which the two halves of the battery could be run in parallel, reducing the voltage to about 40 for slow running during street collection. In practice this turned out to be less essential than anticipated, and when the switch was found to be in the way of the demountable battery crates later introduced it was done away with without detriment to the usefulness or adaptability of the vehicles.

The chassis, as a pressed item in high tensile steel, was a bought-in component, the first twenty being supplied by Macintosh for the unbelievably low price of £21. 0s. 0d. per set though they declined further orders at that price, and the immediately subsequent vehicles had frames by Rubery Owen at £50. 0s. 0d. a set. The overall nett cost, incidentally, of the first ten vehicles was £8 474. 0s. 0d - £847 each compared with an estimated cost per vehicle of £884. The second batch of ten worked out rather better - £810 each - and even after the set back of the increased chassis price when going over to Rubery Owen the third batch came out at only £840 each, against a selling price in each case of £1 070. 0s. 0d. The margin in the latter case covered Works overheads (calculated at 100% on the labour content i.e. £135) and profit, which thus worked out at £95 per vehicle.

The controller was a foot-operated E.M.B. unit giving eight speeds in each direction and was interlocked with the brakes so that the application of either hand or foot brake put the controller back to neutral. Despite the fact that the brakes operated only on the rear wheels they never gave rise to complaint though by the sixties this was another characteristic that marked the GTZ as obsolete. For the final batch there was a tentative proposal to use Lockheed hydraulic brakes but this was not adopted.

Early bodies had open tops covered when travelling by roller shutters which retracted into a central blind box along the spine of the body during loading but later bodies had an all over roof, the side loading apertures being fitted with rubber strip curtains and side shutters to hinge up when each compartment was full. In earlier vehicles the sides hinged at the loading line for emptying purposes but in the final four vehicles the sides were arranged to hinge from the roof in two sections which avoided the irritation of refuse draping itself on the centre rail.

Changing the solid tyred GTZs to pneumatics -which looked so easy in principle - almost foundered over the difficulty of securing sufficient clearance in the wheel arches of the body to allow the body to be tipped and to enable a wheel to be changed. Whereas in the design of body for the solid tyred chassis the body frame could be cranked in the horizontal plane round the back of the wheel it was no longer possible to do this with pneumatics as it would have cut into the top inside edge of the tyre on tipping. Leslie Farrow solved the problem by making the wheel arch a steel fabrication forming part of the body frame. This essential design step, together with modifications to the front and rear hubs, gave just sufficient clearance but it was a close thing. The conversion kits designed by Garretts were incorporated into the solid tyred GTZs as they came up for major overhaul at the Corporation's St. Rollox Works and thus, by bringing them into compliance with the 1934 Road Traffic Act, extended what would otherwise have been limited lives. The use of solid tyres on the earlier vehicles running, as they did, over sett roadways, meant that they took a considerable pounding which, in turn, led to failures of welds on light fabricated items, such as framework to the circuit breakers and switchboard, and flexing of the composite wood and steel framing of the cabs, problems which, once pneumatics were introduced, were much less frequent.

It is a curious phenomenon how many annoyances arise from penny-pinching economies. For instance, in the slow running and battery change over switches of the GTZs the copper contacts were mounted on ³/₈" copper studs through which the current passed. These switches were a bought-in item and one supplier made the economy of substituting steel for copper studs with the result that overheating and charring of the insulation occurred - a classic illustration of the truth behind the axiom 'penny wise, pound foolish', too often dismissed as a mere cliché. However, considering that the GTZs were a twenties design and that for thirty years they were double manned so as to work round the clock, their immunity from serious troubles was remarkable.

When they were new Glasgow Corporation had assigned them a life expectancy of fifteen years. In fact most of them achieved about thirty. Like the trams and the underground they became part of the fabric of the Glasgow scene looked upon by those who drove and maintained them with the same wry affection as that which inspired the underground railway workshop staff by infinite ingenuity and resource to keep their seventy and eighty year old charges running. Inexorably time had run out for all the Glasgow electric rolling stock, though it is a matter for regret that No.57, probably the last big battery electric of its generation to run in revenue earning service, was allowed to end up in the scrap-yard for the paltry sum of £41. 10s. 0d, so low was the preservation interest in battery electrics at that time. The tide of opinion and fashion in the fifties and sixties was running strongly for motors and the oil based economy. Had the same decisions to be taken in the 1990's what might the answer have been? Few in the mid-50's would have said that fifteen years later the Glasgow underground would have had a rebirth. Perhaps, had the cards fallen out differently, electricity generated from refuse in a larger version of Govan power station might yet have supplied current to a fleet of trams, trolley buses and electric lorries.

Fig.103. The last GTZ to run in Glasgow was No.57 (Works No.445), seen here when new outside the erecting shop at the Town Works, before being put on rail. Surprisingly it outlived later examples.

Fig.104. *The scene inside the doors against which No.445 was posed in the preceding illustration - a view eastwards in the erecting shop at the Town Works showing Nos. 450 to 453 being erected - the last GTZs to be built.*

Fig.105. *No.450, first of the final four GTZs, embodied considerable modernisation to the cab, modification of the front axle, roller bearings on the prop shaft, crated batteries, and a general lightening of components, which saved £25 a year in Road Tax but in the end led to their being less rugged and durable than their immediate predecessors.*

Fig.106. *Rear end view of the same vehicle.*

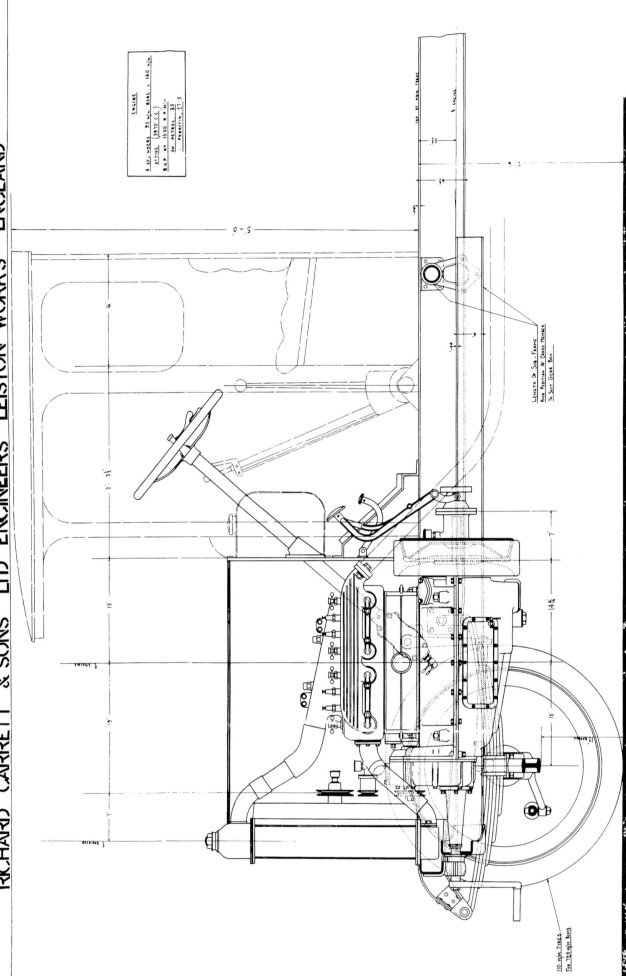

RICHARD GARRETT & SONS LTD ENGINEERS LEISTON WORKS ENGLAND

ENGINE
4 CYL MODEL 95 m/m BORE x 140 m/m
STROKE (3970 C.C.)
B.H.P AT 1500 R.P.M —
ON PETROL 35
— PARAFFIN 27.5

LENGTH OF SUB-FRAME
AND POSITION OF CROSS MEMBER
TO SUIT GEAR BOX

110 m/m TRACKS
FOR 710 m/m RIMS

DRG N.º   KL 20103

N.º 2 ARRANGEMENT

PROPOSED ARRANGEMENT OF 2 TON GARRETT KEGRESSE LORRY

SCALE 3" = 1 FOOT

Chapter 6

The Caledon Episode

The three week long French expedition of Winter 1922/23 across the Sahara in motor vehicles equipped with Kegresse endless rubber tracks, which caught the imagination both of the general public and of the motor and engineering trades, seems also to have fired the minds of some of the senior personnel at Leiston Works as there are a number of sketches and drawings of light trucks on half-tracks, dating from the early and mid 1920's. These led into a series of preliminary arrangement drawings of steam powered half-tracked tractors, already discussed in Part 2. Undoubtedly Plane, himself, must have been fascinated by the thought of 'off-road' transport, but the amount of work put into the drawing up of his concepts is such that it cannot have represented his inclinations alone but rather must have been done under instruction, or at very least, benevolent approval from above. Serious consideration of such proposals must have brought the realisation that vehicles of this type could appeal only to a very restricted market, a high proportion of which was made up of military uses. Coupled with this must have come awareness that the scale of the Leiston operation was too small to sustain such a project in which the odds against success were so heavy. Some other entrée into motor vehicle building had, therefore, to be sought. The recognition that if Richard Garrett & Sons Ltd. or, indeed, the whole of the AGE group, looked for a future in road vehicle production there had to be a move to the internal combustion engine was one that, to their credit, came quite early to both the constituent company board and to the main board. Unfortunately, in the manner that bedevilled so many enterprising moves by AGE, a way to achieve the objective was sought by the back door or on the cheap. It was a besetting sin of AGE that after its initial profligacy, which was written about in Part 2, it over-reacted into a tight-fisted policy that seemed unable to distinguish thrift from parsimony.

Because of this, the initial venture of Leiston Works into motor production was undertaken in what seems, with hindsight, to have been an act of crass folly, the circumstances of which were as follows. From about 1908 until the outbreak of the 1914-18 war, Scottish Commercial Cars Ltd. had been the Scottish agents for Commer vehicles but the relationship was brought to an end by the whole of the Commer output being taken up by the Government for war purposes. As demand continued unabated or even enhanced by the shortages of draught horses and horse feed, the company decided to make vehicles of its own. The brothers Harry and Edmund Tainsh who had been with the Argyll Motor Co. were recruited to design the proposed vehicle and to set up a factory for production. The chain-driven 4-ton lorry they produced was sold as the *Caledon*, built around the Dorman 4JO 40 HP engine and the French Dux patented constant mesh gearbox. During the war and the immediate post-war period of shortage there was no problem in selling all the vehicles that could be produced. Indeed the sales for 1919 reached 170 units, the best annual sales result the firm achieved, but the boom conditions of that freak year led the

Fig.107. (opposite). The leading end of the half-tracked light lorry designed by Maurice Plane in 1923, inspired by the Citroen Kegresse equipped expedition across the Sahara in 1922/23, and
Fig.108. (below) the type of rear bogie (based upon a Delahaye drawing) which it was proposed to use.

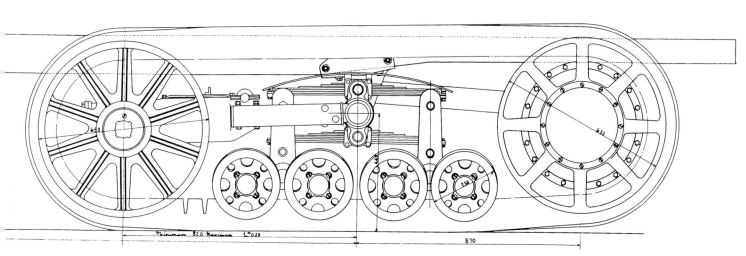

management, as it had led AGE, into the trap of believing that the level of demand was permanent. On the strength of this belief the manufacturing side was separated from the parent company as Caledon Motors Ltd. and thereupon embarked on an ambitious expansion programme covering chassis capacities from 1½ tons to 7 tons, and embracing shaft drive types for bus and coach work. In addition development work was put in hand for a sleeve valved engine. These over ambitious projects combined with the inevitable contraction of sales experienced as the abnormal level of demand was satisfied and the incidence of Government surplus sales to bring the firm near to financial ruin within two years. Scottish Commercial Cars then resumed control to avert total collapse, but by 1926 they had had enough and were seeking a way out of the commitment.

At this time the battery electric business at Leiston had reached a very low point. One wonders who it was at Garretts or, perhaps, at AGE to whom the idea occurred that a take-over of the slender remaining assets of the Caledon marque might provide a cut-price entrée into the motor lorry market. From whatever source the idea emanated, looking back it can be seen to have had too many factors stacked against it to have been made successful. Perhaps the most telling of them was that the Caledon had never been a popular make and had not sold appreciable numbers except under the conditions of a seller's market. In my youth Isaac Beer & Sons Ltd., the London provision merchants, rented a building in Sevenoaks, Kent, from my late uncle for use as a local depot and a garage for Caledon 'D'-type No.392. I had every opportunity, therefore, to study this chain-drive van. It was sturdy, fairly reliable, painfully slow, and outdone in customer appeal by most of its peers. In short, by 1926 a van of this type was obsolescent. Who brokered the deal between Garretts and Scottish Commercial Cars is not known, nor is it known what sums of money were paid for the marque. As a consequence of the deal, concluded about November, 1926, Leiston received a quantity of new parts, a set of working drawings of all models in production, the register of Caledon owners, and the services of Harry Tainsh as a consultant until mid-Summer, 1927. It was the intention at the outset to market seven chassis types. These were the 'B', in long or short versions, to carry 30-40 cwt., the 'C' (3 tons), the 'E' (4tons), and the 'H' (5 tons), all of which were to be worm driven; the 'G' type 5-tonner and the 'F' type 6/7-tonner, both chain driven; and two 6-wheelers - a 10-tonner with double worm drive, and a chain driven 12-tonner. The first three to be built were an 'E' 4-tonner with shaft drive, a 5-ton 'G' chain drive, and a new design to be called the 'Freighter'.

In an internal memorandum to Maurice Plane on February 16, 1927, Arthur Bennett, the then Works Director, said:

<u>CALEDON VEHICLES</u>
Order Office have instructions to issue orders for the following three vehicles:-
      1 - 4-ton Live Axle type Chassis.
      1 - 5-ton Chain-driven type Chassis.
      1 - 'Freighter' type Chassis.
The necessary Drawing Office instructions, prints, schedules, etc. should be issued as quickly as possible through Mr.Thorpe.
For the 4 and 5-ton Chassis, it has been decided to use the 'Dorman' 4.J.O. type engine, and for the Freighter the 'Meadows' Engine and Gearbox you have already shown in your general arrangement of the vehicle.
Mr.Tainsh is getting Thompsons of Wolverhampton to send in the Main Frame Members of both the 4-ton and 5-ton vehicles.
We want to get an early start on this job and to have these three vehicles ready for test as soon as we possibly can using, of course, as far as we can, material that is already in stock.

Of these, the 'E'-type was actually completed and sold - to Scottish Commercial Cars Ltd! It was allocated the Works No.35127, and left the Works on September 20, 1927. The chain-driven 'G'-type 5-tonner was completed but not sold, though it was later used for experimental work in connection with diesel lorries, including a visit to Aveling & Porter at Rochester where it was fitted for a while with one of their 'Invicta' diesel engines undergoing development trials. The visit to Rochester was not the subject of an inter-company sale, and the vehicle remained Garrett property. At the annual audit for the financial year ending March 31, 1930, Aveling & Porter certified that they held on behalf of Richard Garrett & Sons Ltd. 'one Caledon 5-ton petrol lorry.' A year later it was still there but before the time arrived for the 1932 audit the Leiston firm had gone under. The ultimate fate of the lorry was probably to be broken up with the other scrap at Rochester when the Works was cleared.

Whereas the manufacture of these two lorries was mainly an assembly job from existing parts or bought-in components the building of the 'Freighter' meant designing an entirely new type of lorry. This was to be a 2½-ton low wheeled forward control chassis. Had it reached the market, the name 'The Freighter' might have invited a riposte from Shelvoke & Drewry who had been using it for some time to describe their own product with which the new Caledon design was clearly intended to be a competitor. The new lorry was fitted with conventional steering and controls so that in this respect it would not have rivalled the '*SD*', but its low loading line was obviously aimed at attracting back some of the lost trade in refuse collectors which was commented upon at the end of Chapter 2.

So far as the Drawing Office was concerned the management of the work on the Caledons was given to Charles E.Layne who thus had the not altogether enviable task of liaising with Harry Tainsh, nominally through his chief, Maurice Plane. Tainsh appears to have regarded himself as belonging at boardroom level, and frequently seems to have tried to bypass the Drawing office by going straight to Arthur Bennett, a ploy which Bennett was astute enough to avert whenever possible. Sensing that there might be some unwelcome cans to be attached to the tail of any unguarded individual, Layne was careful to refer all of his questions in a series of politely worded letters sent over Plane's signature to Tainsh's private residence at 112, Addison Way, Golders Green, London NW11. It is evident that not all of the parts sent from Glasgow were finished for on June 16, 1927, Plane wrote to Tainsh:

> We shall be glad if you will kindly let us know the correct treatment for the rough steel blanks for the gear box gears that have been sent from Glasgow.

How Tainsh answered this is not known for his next letter (of June 23) makes no reference to the question but dwells at length on points of design in the 'Freighter'. The position of Plane and, in turn, Layne was difficult. On the one hand the firm wished to push forward the making of the 'Freighter' as far as possible before Tainsh's consultancy expired. On the other hand the Drawing office was full of work, whilst Plane was under constant pressure to cut down on manpower and to avoid resorting to staff overtime. Layne, for his part, was heavily committed on the designs for bakers ovens whilst the other senior draughtsmen, Newark and Roe, were fully engaged upon the steam wagon work. There was, therefore, something of a conflict in priorities. However, by February, 1927, the drawings of the 'Freighter' were more or less complete, enabling a prototype to be built. In this a Thompson chassis carried a Meadows 4EH 14HP engine, a Coventry cast aluminium alloy radiator, and a Meadows 5A gear box and worm drive rear axle from a 2 ton Caledon. The cardan shaft had fabric type flexible joints. As an economy Layne had used up a Kirkstall front axle surplus from electric vehicle manufacture. Tainsh, probably rightly, thought this too heavy.

Construction of the 'Freighter' went on so rapidly that by mid-May it was virtually complete. Notwithstanding the fact that only the 'E' and 'G' types and the 'Freighter' were actually in hand it remained the intention soon to supplement the range by building in addition the 3 and 5-ton shaft driven chassis, a 4-ton chain driven chassis to be called the 'D' type, and the 10-ton shaft driven 6-wheeler. All these matters were referred to in Tainsh's letter to Leggett on May 16, 1927. The letter, which was copied and sent to Plane, is set out below with Leggett's comments in the margin.

GARRETT-CALEDON CHASSIS

In view of the decision to only manufacture, in the meantime, a Freighter, 3, 4 and 5 ton live axle chassis, 4 and 5 ton chain-driven chassis, and 10 ton live axle rigid six-wheel chassis, enclosed is a schedule of the Engines which I recommend as being the best for the respective chassis.

With regard to the Freighter, which is almost complete, I have been in collaboration with Mr.Thorpe and looked over this chassis very carefully, and with a view to simplifying and cheapening the

Take note production, I have suggested a number of modifications which ought to be made in the design before this chassis is put into production.

With regard to the standard chassis, certain modifications are required, some of them to be incorporated when present stock of parts is used up. Some details which might be modified to suit the manufacturing facilities in these Works, and some modifications are required, owing to

and this alteration in the design of the J.O.R. Engines which are fitted to the two first chassis. The position of the carburetter and other details of these Engines are different from the old J.O. Engine and this new Engine is designed so that it can be fitted into the frame on the three point suspension system, which will enable us to scrap the Engine sub-frame which formerly had to be used. This entails slight modifications in the frame, and I recommend, after about ten chassis, that an improved and cheaper frame be fitted.

It is essential that these alterations and modifications are gone into thoroughly and the specifications put in order, and I shall be glad if the Drawing Office can get instructions to do so at once, so that I can see that they are quite all right before I leave.

To await results Arrangements should be made to order up material, of which there is a shortage, to enable prompt *of tests on* delivery to be given of certain number of chassis. *chassis* The question of spares also requires to be dealt with at the same time as both material for producing chassis and for spares should go through the Works together.

I have prepared a list showing the Wearing Parts which are in constant demand and am discussing with Mr.Thorpe the quantities which should be put in hand, with a view to economic production with the least expenditure.

Ascertain Mr.	It is important also that the Drawing office go into the drawings of the 10 ton six-wheel chassis,
Tainsh's view and	and arrange for a few sets of parts for this chassis being put in hand so that reasonable delivery
note his remark	could be given when orders are received.
	It was intended that the finish of the chassis be improved on from what was possible in Glasgow built chassis, and I think someone should be instructed to consider these possible improvements in finish, with a view to having them incorporated in all future chassis.
Would Mr.Tainsh	There are very many points in connection with the efficient and economic manufacture of these
put these remarks	Chassis that I should like to give the fullest information on before I leave. I could easily discuss the
on to paper	points of design with the Drawing Office, but there are other points which I think should be gone into by either yourself or Mr.Bennett.

Here again Tainsh is suggesting that there were some matters better discussed with a higher authority than Plane - the habit that earned him so much unpopularity in the Drawing Office. Leggett's comment in the margin against the closing paragraph shows that he did not agree with this attitude.

The 'Freighter' was completed about June, 1927. No exact date is recorded for the event other than that ascribed by the memory of some of those involved. It was tested over the usual Garrett test routes, beginning with a trip to Aldeburgh and back. Two unpalatable facts emerged from the building and testing of this initial vehicle. Firstly it was rather heavy and somewhat greedy on petrol consumption, and secondly the results of work in the Cost Office disclosed that it had been expensive to make, although no exact figure survives. What does survive, however, is the fact that Carrimore Six Wheelers Ltd. of North Finchley, London N12 (by coincidence the adjacent postal district to that in which Tainsh lived) put onto the market a 2-ton low-wheeled truck they called the *Freighter 3000,* a vehicle so closely resembling the Caledon Freighter as to be almost indistinguishable, at the price of £235. 0s. 0d. with which Leiston could not compete. The prototype Caledon Freighter was not sold, therefore, nor even offered for sale, as far as can be traced, but was used by its makers as Works transport for almost the remainder of the firm's life, although as it was not one of the vehicles offered for sale by the Receiver one assumes that it must have been scrapped before the very end. It should perhaps be added that the Carrimore Freighter 3000 had very limited sales. By far the most successful of the low-line trucks was the 'SD', together with the Karrier 'CYR' and its successor the *Bantam.* Between them these two mopped up the greater part of the limited market for low-line vehicles.

With the disappointment over the Freighter appears to have come the realisation that the Caledon range which Leiston had so optimistically proposed to build was incapable of attracting potential buyers away from the major producers. In the Autumn of 1927 the whole project was dropped in favour of a different approach, but one that was still based upon the misleading notion that some cheaper way existed of entering the motor lorry market than that of designing an up-to-date vehicle from first principles. The next line of experiment is described in the ensuing chapter.

Fig.109. No.35127, an E-type, was the only Caledon made at Leiston that was sold. It was sent off on September 20, 1927, to Glasgow.

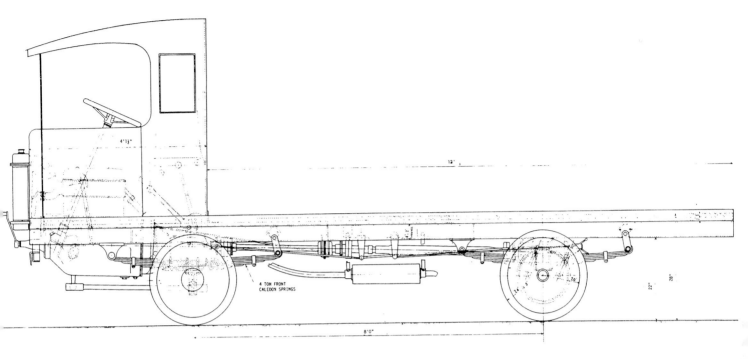

Fig.110. (Plan) and Fig.111 (elevation) of the 2½-ton Caledon Freighter, designed and built at Leiston
- a mish-mash of stock parts, proprietary components, and new material. Never sold, it was used on the
Works for a while as internal transport, using trade plates for its rare ventures onto the public road.

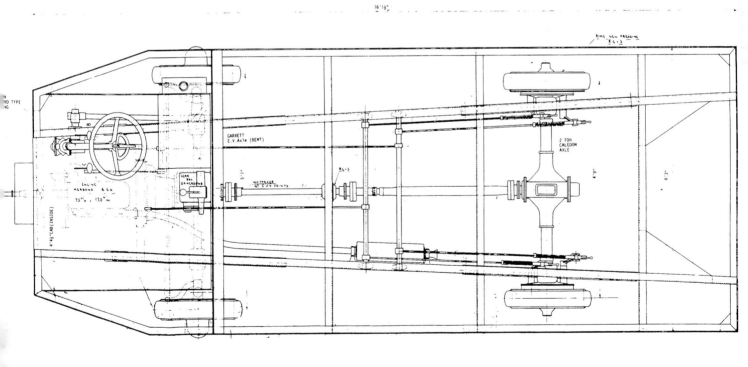

Fig.112. *The* Freighter *as built differed a little from the drawing, most noticeably in the radiator and scuttle.*

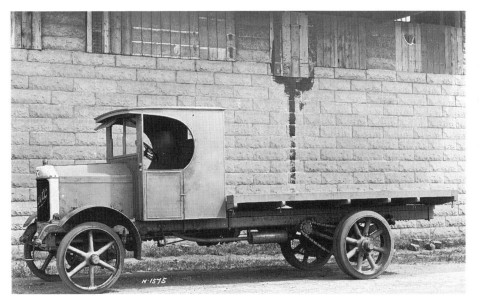

Fig. 113. The chain driven G-type, mainly assembled from parts brought to Leiston from Glasgow, was never sold but was later loaned or hired to Aveling & Porter as a mobile test bed for the Invicta *diesel engine.*

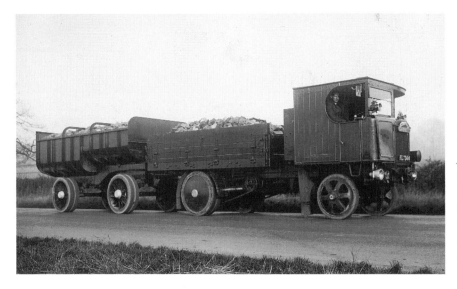

Fig.114. *The four- wheeled* COW *(No.35224), produced by fitting a McLaren Benz oil engine into the chassis and bodywork of a four-wheeled steam wagon, seen here drawing the heavy all-steel tipping trailer. Fred McKeer is at the wheel.*

Chapter 7

The Diesel and Petrol Engined Vehicles

Undeterred by the Caledon episode, the company tackled the motor lorry market from another direction. Because, to its credit, it had perceived the potential of the oil engine as the road power unit of the rest of the century the decision was taken to build diesel engined lorries. Many, the author included, have condemned the AGE management as inept. Here, by contrast, they were right and ahead of their time.

The first design produced, however, was for a solid tyred six-wheeled chassis, using a McLaren Benz three cylinder oil engine, a Leiston designed gearbox, a countershaft with differential, roller chain final drive, and a cab resembling the ill fated 'Freighter'. Most of this, except the power unit, was thoroughly dated. The general arrangement drawing, QL23831, dated July 16, 1928, is reproduced on page 98. This scheme was dropped in favour of an adaptation of the QL steam wagon designs to oil propulsion. Though one cannot now be certain why this was, it seems probable that the sales staff might have doubted its sales potential. Moreover James Garvie, a notoriously impatient man, was newly arrived on the Leiston scene and may have pressed for a more rapid method of producing a vehicle in which an oil engine could be tried. Using steam wagon components certainly speeded things up and had the advantage that in the event of total failure, they could be rebuilt as steamers, a good way to minimise the risk. The transition of the QL wagons from steam to oil was accomplished by leaving unaltered the chassis frame, axles, wheels, water tank, cab, and bodywork, but putting the McLaren Benz diesel engine in the cab in the space formerly taken up by the boiler, with a gear box, short cardan shaft, countershaft and final drive as in the first scheme. A cast aluminium alloy radiator was fitted into the front apron plate. The limited amount of new drawing work was divided between Charles Newark, Charles Layne, and some junior draughtsmen, and drawn in pencil on tracing paper, many drawings being issued to the Works on the day they were drawn. Thus the arrangement drawings of the six-wheeler, drawn by Charles Layne, and the four-wheeler, by Charles Newark, were finished on September 19, 1928, and issued to the Works the same day. Most of the other drawings, including the cab layout and detailed drawings of the gearbox, short cardan shaft and countershaft, were finished within the ensuing month and all were printed and issued on the day they were completed. Because of the experimental factor, the building completion date is tentative - mid-Autumn 1928 seems probable, though *ex tempore* amendments followed. The job has all the hallmarks of having been worked out as construction proceeded.

The engine selected for the 4-wheeled wagon was two-cylindered, giving a power output of 30-35 BHP at 800 r.p.m., the normal maximum. This engine had been applied with success to such machines as small excavators, locomotives, and items of fixed plant but in practice it was found to be too small for the Garrett wagon. As no electric starter was fitted the engine took a great deal of effort to start by hand. The late Frank Waddell recalled seeing four or five men on a rope pulling the starting handle over time after time, helped on by Garvie using his notable command of invective. Frequently starting was effected by sending for any steam wagon that happened to be in steam and resorting to towing. The McLaren Benz engines, once started, were great stickers and would plod on indefinitely with heavy loads or up steep hills, slow, noisy, and sounding all the while as if each revolution would be the last, but never actually giving up. Fred McKeer who, among others, drove them on their test runs, developed a grudging admiration for them despite the racket in the cab. The title given to the pair was 'Crude Oil Wagons' and the acronym by which they were known to the staff was *COWS,* said to refer as much to their behavioural characteristics as to the title on the drawings!

For the six-wheeler the four cylinder engine was chosen, having virtually double the power output of the two cylinder engine. This made for a much livelier performance on the road, improved still further when a belt driven blower was fitted to it. The problem of starting was tackled by fitting a Douglas two stroke petrol engine as a starting auxiliary. According to Fred McKeer this made life much easier. The six-wheeler was given the Works No.35223 whilst the other wagon became No.35224, the carrying capacities being rated respectively at 15 and 6 tons. Both, however, were capable of drawing a 12 ton all-steel trailer, built at the same time as the wagons, though, of course, the law prohibited the 6-wheeler from doing so on the road, and the 4-wheeler was very slow when hauling it.

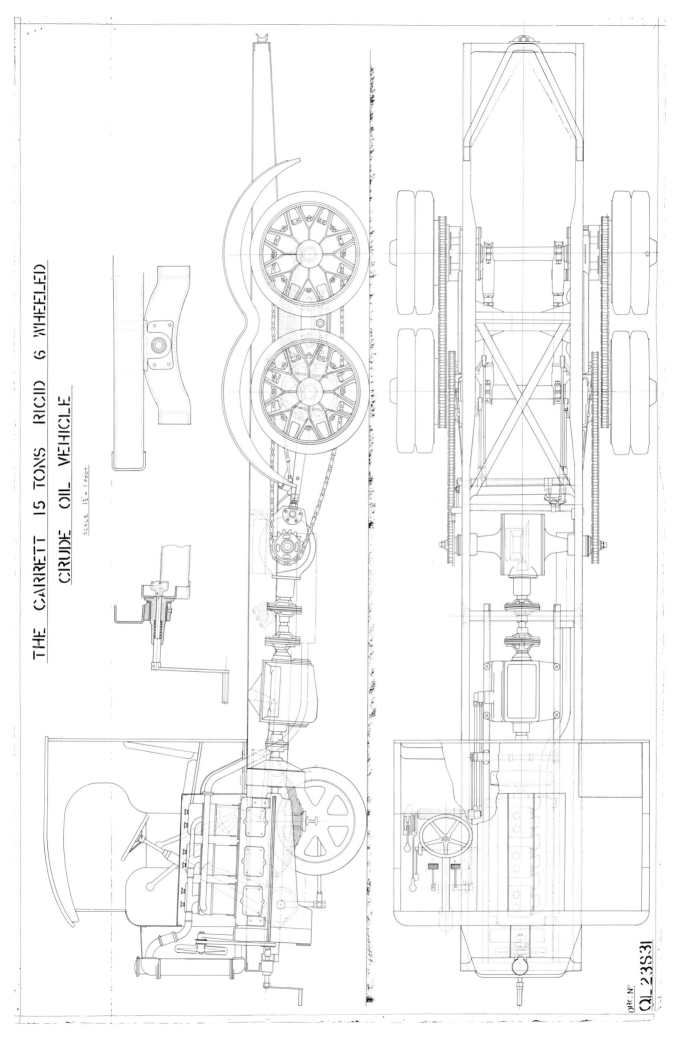

THE GARRETT 15 TONS RIGID 6 WHEELED

CRUDE OIL VEHICLE

SCALE 1½ = 1 FOOT

DRG. N° QL 23S·31

Fig.115. *The elevation and* **Fig.116.** *the plan of the first version of the oil-engined COW 6-wheeler.*

98

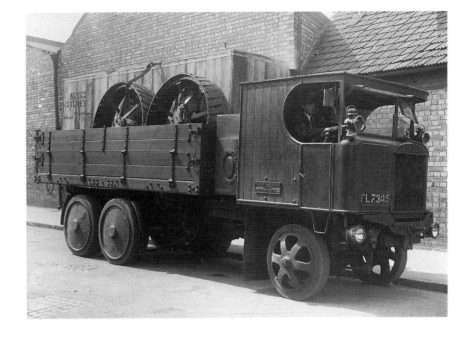

Fig.117. *The larger of the two COWs, again with Fred McKeer driving, despite the fact that the owner's plate on the cab-side proclaims it to be the property of Barford & Perkins of Peterborough.*

Fig.118. *Notwithstanding its uncomely appearance No.35224 was capable of useful work and is seen here when it, too, was in the hands of Barford & Perkins, the load being a motor roller crated for export.*

Fig.119. *The nearside elevation of the GB6 lorry.*

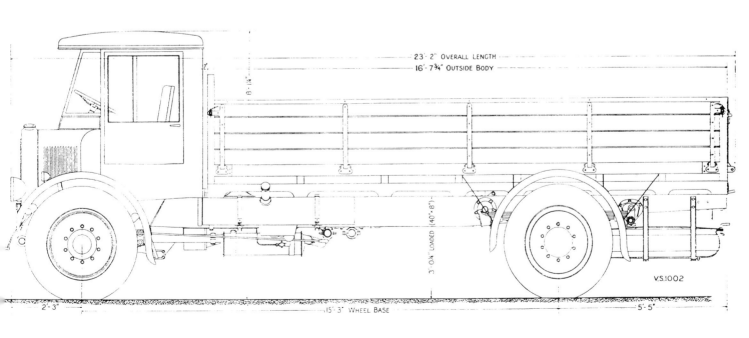

99

No serious attempt seems to have been made to market them in this country although the 6-wheeler was demonstrated to a party of potential buyers from South Africa. It was arranged that the delegation should visit Leiston Works where they were entertained to lunch. The wagon carried the test load of fifteen 1-ton concrete blocks bolted to the chassis. To accommodate the party, seats were roped to the blocks for ten of them to sit on. The eleventh visitor, whom Fred recalled as wearing a wide brimmed Stetson hat, rode in the cab. This proved to be a mistake. When the windscreen was opened to keep down the cab temperature the wind snatched the hat from its owner's head and into the drive belt of the blower where it was reduced to oily debris. Nor did the remainder of the demonstration go without incident. The lorry was taken round one of the standard test routes, from Leiston to Theberton, on via Middleton and Yoxford to Saxmundham and back to Leiston. With an unladen weight of 12 tons the lorry plus load weighed 27 tons apart from the passengers and driver. Anxious to give the best impression of its performance Fred wished to get up the rise at Middleton in top gear, for which reason he took a corner rather too fast and lost some of his rear-seat passengers overboard, depositing them over a hedge and into a cabbage patch, by great good fortune uninjured. No sale resulted from the demonstration.

The two lorries were sold to fellow AGE members, Barford & Perkins. Though intended to leave Leiston on November 1, 1928, they did not in fact go until early January, 1929. At first sight, the circumstances of the sale suggest that it was a face-saving transaction designed by accountants to disguise a loss, but this was not the truth as the wagons were put to commercial use by their owners, registered as FL 7344 (the 4-wheeler) and FL 7345. Wilf Cole, the joint owner and operator of a number of Garrett undertype wagons in Leeds, once recounted to me how he had encountered one of them in that hilly part of Yorkshire, recalling that his attention was first caught by the noise of its distant approach. His eyes were then puzzled by the spectacle of what seemed to be a steam wagon making such a racket. When seen more closely it revealed its secret and despite the din seemed to be making good progress. At least one Garrett steamer was later converted to diesel power by Pelican Engineering in Leeds, using a Gardner engine.

Notwithstanding the shortcomings of the two lorries, realised at least as much by their builders as by outside observers, they were the first British built lorries to be fitted with oil engines from new, anticipating by about a year that other notable pioneer effort, the Kerr Stuart, launched onto the market in 1929 using the same engine and method of starting as the 6-wheeled Garrett, though it was designed *de novo* rather than as an adaptation of an existing design as were the Garretts.

From the point of view of the Works technical staff the trials with these two lorries established that the automotive diesel engine was a practical proposition once the refining of its detail and the solution of some design problems had been carried out. To the boardrooms of the daughter companies and of the holding company the problems of company politics entered the equation. Between them these boardrooms required the services of thirty-seven directors, many of whom - perhaps as many as two-thirds - were members or descendants of the founding families and felt it their inherent duty to uphold the integrity of the 'family' works. Whilst it is to their collective credit that they were persuaded of the future of diesel propulsion, in the implementation of this policy, with which the majority of directors broadly agreed, rifts began to appear.

Aveling & Porter had in hand the development of a diesel engine of their own design, discussed at some length in *Garrett Diesel Tractors*. On the other hand, Blackstones of Stamford had long been manufacturers of oil engines for land use, derivatives of which had been used in road rollers. Their chief designer was Evershed Carter, nick-named 'Tod', a man of immense experience in the field of fixed engines. Again Davey Paxman in Colchester were embarked upon building larger oil engines for stationary applications, notably pumping and electricity generation. In the atmosphere of cliques, temporary alliances, and back-room diplomacy that prevailed in the upper reaches of AGE affairs, the claims of this trio of makers overcame with ease any suggestion that Garretts might themselves develop a diesel engine or purchase a proprietary unit from outside the group. Further bartering on the main board led to the unsatisfactory solution that both Avelings and Blackstones should be allowed to proceed with the manufacture of automotive diesels. As to the building of the vehicle in which the completed engine was to be carried Garretts were deemed to have the best claim, and thus it was established that a completely fresh design of lorry, on the most modern lines, would be prepared in the Leiston Drawing Office whilst at Stamford Blackstones produced the engine that was to power it. The actual designing and developing of the Blackstone automotive diesel was mainly in the hands of Tod Carter's younger brother,

Fig.120. No.35455 (the original GB6) in the Erecting Shop, Town Works. Behind it are three diesel engined tractors (Nos.35445, 35446, and 35448) and in the foreground Garrett traction engine No.35461 and Burrell No.4093. [S.R.O.]

Fig.121. The improvement in chassis design over the preceding decade is illustrated by the picture of electric vehicle No.130 at the 1920 Royal Show. Behind it is No.33781, the 50 BHP direct ploughing traction engine. [S.R.O.]

Frank. At Aveling & Porter the diesel engine developments were the province of Frank Perkins, who later built up the immensely successful Perkins diesel engine firm in Peterborough.

In the Drawing Office some thought was given to the production of a design of lorry in which steam power or diesel power could be offered as alternatives, perhaps reflecting parallel thinking at the Foden works where many chassis and running gear components were in common between the Speed 6 and the first production run of diesel engined lorries. An illustration of the steam version of this tentative project appeared as Fig.112 in Part 2. No agreement appears to have been reached to carry either the steam or the diesel version to the stage of detailed design work.

These discussions and dissensions at both board room and drawing office levels rumbled on for a long time. By mid-1930 the trading position was bad and showing signs of becoming much worse not only because of the general decline in trade which became the Slump but also because, more specifically to the heavy vehicle business, the arrival of new draft Ministry of Transport regulations on axle loadings and the realisation that in future enforcement was likely to be strict made the prospects for steam wagons seem very poor indeed. However, the sounds emanating from the works at Rochester and Stamford on the success of their respective efforts in developing oil engines suitable for use in lorries had become progressively more encouraging as 1930 unfolded. On October 28, 1930, the five executive directors of Richard Garrett & Sons Ltd., namely Leggett, Bennett, Cheadle, Garvie, and Ryan, sat round the boardroom table at Leiston Works to consider how to set up a project to provide a vehicle in which these engines could be used. Cheadle, with refreshing directness and lack of cant, summarized later the findings of the directorial committee setting out the basic premises from which they had worked:

> There was general agreement as to the desirability and urgent need of producing a 4-wheeled pneumatic-tyred Heavy Oil Engined Vehicle at Leiston, equipped with a six-cylinder Blackstone Engine. An attempt was then made to explore the best method of setting about this, and to ascertain the time required, after which the estimated expense, which would be involved, was broadly considered. As to the method of procedure, alternative courses seemed to suggest themselves. Firstly, to purchase a good example of a modern Heavy Oil Engined chassis, to copy that exactly, and to proceed with the manufacture of it at Leiston, procuring the Engine, of course, from Stamford. Alternatively, there is the method of buying the separate components from reputable makers of such and assembling them in a chassis which, as to its other features, would be designed and made at Leiston. The balance of opinion was in favour of the latter proposal. It was agreed that, in either case, an experienced Designer of Heavy Internal Combustion Engined Vehicles would be necessary to supervise activities in that direction. The objective is, of course, to produce ultimately all such components at Leiston as can be made there economically. As to the time required, it was estimated that, if an immediate decision was arrived at and instructions given, the first Vehicle could be ready for trial during January (Messrs. Blackstone could deliver a suitable engine in about three weeks from the present date) and it is estimated we should be in a position to take orders for such Vehicles during the month of March.
> As already indicated, the first model contemplated is one to carry 6/7 tons payable load on a platform Body. In our opinion, the ultimate objective should be to produce a Wagon capable of carrying payable loads up to 10/12 tons, as it is for this type we would expect the heaviest demand. Such a Wagon would require an Engine of at least 100/120 H.P. It is understood that a suitable Engine could be produced in approximately six months, if Messrs. Blackstone would entertain the proposal.
> In regard to the cost of the programme as outlined for the 6/7 ton Vehicle, it is estimated that the cost of the first Vehicle, including its Body, Engine and such patterns, blocks, dies, etc., as were needed initially would amount to £1500., and that the cost of the second, third and fourth Wagons would be approximately £1200. each. An allowance of approximately £100. should suffice for the road testing of the first Vehicle. In addition to this there would, of course, be the salary of the Designer, which is estimated at the rate of £500. per annum.
> In respect to the subsequent manufacture of the components of the Vehicles in the Works at Leiston, except for such items as the Engine, certain Gears, but including the expenditure of patterns, dies, jigs, etc., (and to put the job on a manufacturing basis) would involve a further expenditure of approximately £2,500. The estimated cost of producing the four demonstration Wagons, and the expenditure on initial advertising would total approximately £5000. The annual sales expenditure would probably be of the same order as now obtains in the case of our Steam Wagon sales. The potential market being greater, the selling cost per Wagon may be considered to be less.
> A review of the manufacturing capacity of the Works at Leiston shows that, without additional plant, but building the components there - except for the Engine and certain Gears, as before enumerated, and assuming also the manufacture of Tractors is carried on at the same time - the Works is capable of dealing with an output of three Vehicles and three Tractors per week.
> With regard to the cost of production, it is estimated that the Chassis can be produced for about £1100., which would cover appropriate overhead charges, plus a reasonable profit. The gross price to customer would be about £1350., which would provide for agents' commission and or selling expenses.

The course the five had agreed to follow paralleled closely that adopted subsequently by E.R.Foden in producing the E.R.F. lorries, but they had very much underestimated the time required to implement their decision. In the event the design was produced by the staff already employed in the Leiston Drawing Office under Maurice Plane, the chief draughtsman, perhaps because of economics alone but, again,

Figs.122. (top) and 123. (centre). In order to study the effect of the proposed cab design for the GB6 a full-size model, mainly of wood and cardboard, was built at the East end of the Drawing Office.

Fig.124. (below). The Blackstone BHV6 engine, used in the GB6 lorry. In spite of their good reputation in the making of fixed oil engines Blackstones did not make a success of developing an automotive diesel engine, and withdrew from the contest in the mid-thirties.

possibly because the attempt to build the Caledons with Tainsh playing the part of the 'experienced designer of heavy internal combustion engined vehicles' had not produced encouraging results as, doubtless, Maurice Plane was quite likely to have pointed out. Nor, as events turned out, did the reserve of £100 for testing the prototype have much relation to the actual monies required.

Frank Carter's diesel engine, titled the B.H.V.6 and effectually an extended version of the 4 cylinder engine put into the diesel tractors, was scheduled to be ready for testing at Leiston in the Spring of 1931. A 6-ton chassis and cab were put in hand at Leiston to meet the projected delivery date of the engine. When work actually began on the project is hard to say with certainty - December, 1930, is probably about right. The drawing list (No.720) is dated April 9, 1931, but this is no aid at all in fixing the date when construction commenced as the drawings were made and altered as work went on, and the list represented only a summary of what had been done rather than a statement of intention. The construction went on in great secrecy and a certain amount of 'disinformation' was allowed to circulate. When writing *Garretts of Leiston* in 1960/64 I was assured that many chassis components of the 4-wheeled steam wagon were used but subsequent research has shown that this was not actually the case and that with trivial exceptions, mostly from electrics and the Caledons, the lorry represented an entirely new venture.

Since weight had been the downfall of the undertype steam wagons and it was anticipated that future enforcement of the permitted axle loadings would be severe great efforts were made in designing the lorry to reduce the unladen weight to a minimum. One of the casualties of this search for weight reduction was the compensating gear in the braking system. The use of hydraulic brakes was not contemplated, the entire braking effort coming from the driver's foot via the levers and rodding. The writer of the descriptive leaflet produced for the launching of the new lorry said, somewhat disingenuously, of this arrangement 'All compensating gear is eliminated as the necessary adjustment for the brakes is provided by wing nuts, which are easily accessible'!

The first lorry of the intended batch of four was allocated the Works No.35455. It had a bought-in pressed chassis of high tensile steel. The wheels were Dunlops, with ten stud fixings, carrying 40" x 8" pneumatics all round, those at the rear being twins. As on the undertype steam wagons and the trolley buses all wheels ran on Timken roller bearings. The front axle was a steel forging, probably by Kirkstall, and the king pins had roller races and bronze bearings. The foot brake worked on all four wheels, the hand brake acting on separate shoes in the rear drums only. The drive was taken by a single plate clutch to a four speed and reverse gearbox with gate change and having ball or roller bearings to all gears, both clutch and gearbox being made by David Brown. The drive continued through tubular cardan and prop shafts to a David Brown worm drive on the rear axle, the shafts being fitted with the American 'Mechanics' joints, marketed in this country by Benjamin Whittaker Ltd. The chassis was grease lubricated via Tecalemit nipples. Electrical equipment was by C.A.V., all 24 volt. Electric starting was used for the first time on a Leiston built vehicle. The lorry had an electric horn, dip and switch headlamps, two sidelights, a tail lamp, and a panel illuminating light on the dashboard, the equipment of which included a speedometer, ammeter, oil pressure gauge, and a plug for an inspection lamp lead, all of which was 'State of the Art' equipment for a 1931 commercial.

Particular attention had been paid to the design of the cab, of which a full-size mock-up, panelled in cardboard, was constructed in the Drawing Office and used as a basis for discussion and modification. It was widely realised, even if not always spoken of, that the diesel lorry represented the company's last chance of survival and the feeling of involvement was intense. The cab design as finally settled upon provided a fully forward driving position with the mate's side recessed back so as to give some access to the engine compartment through a short length of louvred bonnet on the near side. All windows were fitted with Triplex safety glass, and reasonably comfortable seating was installed.

While the prototype was in the closing weeks of its assembly, Richard Cheadle had prepared a document at the Works, dated March 18, 1931, setting out how he believed the testing and marketing of the wagon should be done:

CRUDE OIL WAGON

In order to avoid the possibility of a repetition of troubles similar to those experienced with the Six-Wheeler Steam Wagon, it is considered essential that the first vehicle should undergo an adequate test under working conditions prior to its being put into manufacture and offered for sale. It is, therefore, desirable that a definite procedure should be followed and arrangements made as to the policy to be adopted for subsequent manufacture and sale.

With this object in view, the following suggestions are put forward for the consideration of the Board, so that the arrangements can be made well beforehand.

It is anticipated that the first vehicle will be ready for test about the end of April, following which it is recommended that:-

[1]   A competent person should be placed in charge and made responsible for carrying out working tests, making observations and collecting data.

[2]   The test should consist of at least 10,000 miles, preferably 15,000, under average working conditions.

[3]   At the end of the first 5,000 miles a preliminary report should be made of the results obtained.

[4]   An estimate should then be made of the probable sales for the first six months.

[5]   Prices should be obtained from the various suppliers for quantities as indicated by the prospective sales, and an estimate of the cost of producing the vehicles on this basis should then be prepared, and a provisional selling price fixed.

[6]   A manufacturing programme based on these quantities should be considered and approximate dates fixed for delivery of the vehicles subject to the satisfactory conclusion of the tests.

[7]   The method of marketing should be decided upon, i.e., either by direct representation or through agents or a combination of both methods.

[8]   Preliminary sales data and literature should be prepared.

[9]   On conclusion of the tests a full report should be made and the vehicle dismantled for exhaustive examination.

[10[If found satisfactory, the vehicle be then released for demonstration purposes, and the necessary sales data and literature completed and distributed.

Almost simultaneously a memorandum on the same subject appeared from Bobby Fisher in the London office, dated March 17. This, too, is quoted verbatim as it does show that the problems of getting the lorry a niche in the market were understood:

<u>SUGGESTIONS FOR THE MARKETING OF CRUDE OIL LORRIES</u>

With reference to the writer's conversation with Mr. Cheadle last week to the effect that we should be formulating our plans for the marketing of the Crude Oil Lorry, I am putting forward a few suggestions which I think might be helpful in making preliminary arrangements, because it must be remembered that the Crude Oil Lorry is rather a different proposition to the Steam Wagon, and for this reason we shall be entering a somewhat different market, necessitating to a certain extent different methods of selling.

<u>Tests</u>

Assuming that the first lorry - a standard pneumatic tyred four-wheel six-tonner - has completed its preliminary tests and is ready for the main reliability tests of 20.000 miles, or whatever distance is decided upon, I would suggest that the route is carefully chosen to include such test hills as 'The cat and fiddle' and other gradients in the Peak District of Derbyshire, also that a relay of drivers is provided so that the wagon can run continuously night and day, if necessary. It is a debatable point whether the final part of the tests should not be carried out in different districts - the Representatives having been advised beforehand.

This would be useful from an advertisement point of view and would certainly create a good deal of interest. It would be advisable, however, for the preliminary and reliability tests to be carried out 'incognito' - that is to say, the wagon should not bear any name at all, and the drivers should be instructed to preserve secrecy.

<u>Preparation of selling literature</u>

During the tests referred to, we should be preparing our advance selling literature, and here I would suggest that this takes the form of an attractive folder-leaflet (somewhat on the lines of that used for the Howard Loco), produced in photogravure, only with the text matter, etc. on rather different lines, i.e., to give more actual selling data. We should also produce an issue of *The Garrett Gazette* dealing with the Crude Oil Lorry, its advantages, photographs of lorries on test, etc., and these two publications should be sent out to the approximately 4,000 firms on our Mailing List, as soon as the tests are complete and the first wagon is ready for actual working demonstrations. This leaflet should not be an expensive item and we still have two issues of the *Gazette* in hand under the present contract.

<u>Advertising and Press Demonstration</u>

After the completion of the tests and before the wagon is sent out on demonstration work, the Press Demonstration should be arranged. Representatives of about six of the leading Transport and Engineering papers should be asked to attend. Concurrently with this, full-page advertisements should be prepared in these different papers to appear in the same issue as the account of the demonstration and appropriate advertisements should appear thereafter at regular intervals in these journals. Here again, the expenditure under this heading need not be a very big item, as we already have advertisements appearing in four of these papers, and all that would be necessary under the heading of Advertising would be a slightly larger appropriation, at any rate at the commencement.

<u>Demonstration Wagons</u>

At least two demonstration wagons should be provided, one for the Northern Area and the other for the South. These wagons would be allocated to representatives in rotation, say 2/3 weeks at a time in each area, the programme being so arranged not to interfere with any current enquiries that may be on hand at the time.

<u>Demonstrations</u>

In view of the fact that the Crude Oil Lorry is a high class of wagon when compared with the present type of Steam Wagon, a correspondingly higher class of demonstration driver will be required. The present type of Steam Wagon driver would not be suitable for this purpose. The demonstrator in charge of these lorries should be a man of intelligence, who can not only demonstrate the capabilities of the lorry but also explain in detail the various working parts, more particularly the engine, as this is a comparatively new type of engine to be used on road transport work.

In order to acquire such knowledge, it might be advisable for the demonstrators and also the representatives who are going to handle the sale of the lorries, to spend a day or two at Messrs. Blackstone's works in order to become thoroughly conversant with the Crude Oil Engine.

Prices and Deliveries

In order to arrive at an accurate selling price based on the manufacture in appropriate quantities, it will be necessary to estimate the number of these wagons which could be sold over a given period of say 12 months. This is a very difficult figure to determine, as it has yet to be proved that the Crude Oil Lorry can be sold freely at a price of some £200-£300 greater than that of the modern petrol vehicle, which in itself is a very high class machine. In view of this fact and the other difficulties likely to arise, it would seem advisable to err on the low side, and say approximately 50 in the first year, and this only provided that a tipping model is available after say the first six months.

On the subject of the selling prices I would suggest that a gross fixed selling price is decided upon, and any concessions in price such as reduction for payment in cash, special terms to large users, reduced prices for quantity orders, should be quoted in the form of a discount.

It will also be necessary to gauge fairly accurately when we can commence deliveries, bearing in mind the state of the market today, because the majority of firms will not buy new vehicles today unless they are urgently required or unless they have to replace old wagons which 'are on their last legs'.

Representation and the advisability of selling through Agents

The question of representation is an all-important one. We have at the present time seven outside representatives and it is obvious that if we are to adopt the plan of selling by direct representation, we could not cover the whole of England with seven men. Consequently, it might be advisable to consider appointing agents who even if they did not actually complete the sale on their own, could at any rate introduce the enquiries to us and act as 'scouts' in the district.

There are many points to be said for and against selling through agents, but on the whole I think it would be worth our while to try this method.

Some difficulty will no doubt be experienced in obtaining suitable agents, because the large and influential firms will already be representing firms of petrol vehicle manufacturers, but at the same time, there are a number of smaller firms in the country who ought to be prepared to handle a good 100% British Crude Oil Lorry.

About the same number of Representatives will still be required to work with the Agents, arranging demonstrations and following up enquiries. As to whether the present men are suitable for this work must be left for the Management to decide - a great deal will depend on how much authority is to be given to these Representatives.

The idea of utilising Agents would be to start in the larger towns such as London, Birmingham, Manchester, Sheffield, Liverpool, Leeds, Cardiff, Bristol, Nottingham, etc. extending gradually to the smaller towns and outlying districts, thereby gradually building up a chain of agents throughout the country.

For this reason, Agents could only be allowed a comparatively small territory, and as remuneration would be entitled to a fixed discount, this discount possibly varying if the Agents are prepared to take financial responsibility and/or attend to their own Hire Purchase arrangements.

Part Exchange and Hire Purchase Business

If the sale of Crude Oil Lorries is to be developed to any extent in the Home Market, it will, of course, be necessary to undertake part exchange business, more particularly in petrol lorries, and also be in a position to offer the usual facilities for Hire Purchase business.

Spare Part Agents and Service Inspectors

Spare Part Agents will be required in the same way as in the Steam Wagon business and here it might be possible to arrange for the larger Agents to act as Spare Part Stockists on agreed terms.

Service Inspectors will be necessary, at any rate at the commencement until the lorry becomes firmly established. A great deal will depend on the degree of reliability or otherwise of the Crude Oil Engine. About three Inspectors should be sufficient to start with and the numbers could be augmented, if necessary, as the sales increase.

There will be many other problems to be settled from time to time, but the foregoing may be said to constitute the main headings which have to come under review in order to decide the sales policy in connection with this new product.

One of this initial batch of four was designed with heavier springs and 40" x 9" tyres, for an 8-ton nominal pay-load, to be powered by a proprietary petrol engine, the choice of which fell upon the Meadows 6EX. Construction of this lorry (the drawings for which were summarized in list No.755, dated as late as October 6, 1931) proceeded during the Spring and early Summer of 1931, the dates of the test runs of the two prototypes overlapping one another to some extent. A test team was made up from the Leiston staff under J.K.Peecock, by then the head of the Testing Department. Cyril and Jack Plane, the sons of Maurice Plane, were selected to be observers and reporters and also, tacitly, the spokesmen who headed off unwanted enquiries on the road. Cyril was on the Leiston staff and was newly returned from introducing the new Cormorant decorticator to Jamaica. Jack was working for Blackstones under Frank Carter. Others enlisted were Fred McKeer, H.Woolnough, who had been involved with the trolley buses, A.Burrows and W.Lankester. For book-keeping purposes some of this team was allocated to Blackstones. Bill Lankester, for instance, was charged as a Blackstone man. Blackstones also contributed a very patient and experienced mechanic, Bob Storey.

This group formed a very strong test team of which Peecock became a distinguished leader. On April 27, 1931, he drew up a memorandum of his ideas:

THE CRUDE OIL WAGON
SUGGESTIONS CONCERNING ROAD TESTS

After erecting, adjusting and weighing, (the chassis and cab weighed separately from the body) trial runs for three or four days should be made locally, and the necessary experimenting with the brake gear completed.

Should recommend a general examination be made and the design of the whole vehicle criticized. After an agreement has been reached, all alterations should be made before further testing.

It is understood that the vehicle will be run for the whole of the test period without any advertising, or even the Firm's name appearing. The Secretary's name will be printed in inconspicuous letters.

Suggest approximately three weeks' running in Derbyshire (Snake Hill, Cat & Fiddle, etc., etc.) with practically continuous running day and night and Sundays, to determine hill climbing capabilities, and general robustness. The load carried to be the maximum legal load, and will be ascertained after the vehicle has been weighed. A run of at least 1,000 miles should be made with a 25% overload.

Then should follow several long continuous runs, London-Glasgow, London-Bristol, London-Penzance via Porlock, with the vehicle loaded one way and light for the return. These runs will determine fuel consumption, and general behaviour under normal conditions.

General inspection of the complete vehicle should be made daily and condition logged. The chassis and engine should be dismantled for inspection after each 5,000 miles, and a report made.

A daily log-book should be kept, and all observations entered, together with brief particulars of day's work on the vehicle. The following should be carefully recorded daily:- Fuel and engine lubricating oil consumption; mileage; weather and road conditions; driver, and supplies such as grease, gearbox and rear axle oil, renewals, etc.

Among other things, the steering, clutch and gearbox operation, springing, accessibility and general manoeuvring of the vehicle should be reported on, and the turning circle measured.

The engine performance should be recorded over the entire speed range, particularly at low speeds. Acceleration and deceleration tests should be made under different speed, road and loading conditions.

When the vehicle gives satisfaction, a test should be made with a trailer and load.

At the conclusion of these tests, the vehicle and engine should be completely dismantled and every part carefully examined.

The general procedural parts of his plan were accepted in full, but after discussion it was decided for long distance trials to base the first diesel vehicle at J.& F. Howard's works at Bedford and to run it twice daily round a circular route via Buckingham, Banbury, Stratford, Evesham, and Deddington, from whence the route was the same through Buckingham back to Bedford.

As he had suggested, however, the first trials took place over local roads in the Leiston area used for road testing the steam wagons and electric vehicles. After these preliminary or routine tests No.35455 was painted in Royal blue and finished to Royal Show specification for exhibition at the Royal Show commencing on July 7. The preliminary tests had already led to a number of changes. The gearbox had been smashed as a result of an accident and had to be replaced. In addition, the accelerator, clutch and foot brake pedals with their attendant mechanism were scrapped and replaced by parts of a new pattern. Altogether, according to the Cost Book these changes and prettying up for the Show cost £375 .0 . 4½. Since the nett original cost of the whole vehicle had amounted to £1122 .6 .8., the remedial and beauty treatment must have been of a fairly radical nature.

The first serious reliability test run was on July 26, 1931, when the lorry was taken by Fred McKeer and Cyril Plane, as observer and driver respectively, on a 124½ miles journey via Ipswich and Cambridge to the Blackstone works at Stamford so that Frank Carter might see it at work. This run took 6 hours 4 minutes, an average of 20.6 m.p.h. with a fuel consumption of almost exactly 10 miles to the gallon. Prior to leaving on this run a cover had been fitted on the driver's side of the engine to reduce the noise in the cab which had been found to be nearly unbearable. The new clutch arrangement ran into minor trouble when the forked lever fouled a bolt head on this new engine cover causing the pedal to stick. The next morning, after a demonstration to a Brazilian potential buyer, the lorry was taken down to Ketton Cement Works, who owned the Garrett undertype steam wagon which was subsequently converted to diesel on the lines of the COWS. After lunch a run was made to Northampton and back. Already dark exhaust had begun to be put out when the engine was worked hard. On Tuesday, July 28, the wagon returned to Leiston having first done a morning trip to Grantham and back, and a short demonstration run for a South African firm, Campbell & Carter, interested in the potential agency business. The run was relatively uneventful - an oil leak on the steering box showed itself, and an involuntary stop had to be made at Ipswich to clean out the fuel filter as fluffy material had found its way in, probably with the fuel. This meant that the last part of the journey was made in the dark, during which the bulbs in one sidelamp and the dashboard lamp failed. At that point there were 888 miles on the clock.

On July 29 the lorry was tidied up, during which work it was found that the bulb on the dashboard was, to quote, 'very inaccessible'. As traces of the mysterious fluff were found in the engine oil filter the crankcase was drained, washed out, and refilled. Repairs were made to a battery post damaged by arcing from a loose terminal clamp. After all this the team set out to bring the mileage to 1000 by a return trip to Norwich. The opportunity was taken on this trip to get Burrows accustomed to driving the diesel lorry, his previous experience having been all with steam. From then on the objective was to get the vehicle in good trim for the Cotswold test circuit the following week. On the Thursday (July 30) it did seven runs round the 20 mile road circuit on which the steam wagons were habitually tested. Before starting, the hand brakes needed adjustment, and a short on the horn circuit had to be found and put right. Friday's journey was a trip to Wells, Norfolk, by way of Lowestoft and Yarmouth. The steering column was found to move to and fro when full lock was applied; another battery terminal clamp worked loose causing arcing and damage to the post; the clutch began to slip; and the fuel filters had to be cleaned twice because of fuel contamination. As Peecock noted with exasperation ' This is not a nice or simple job, because all the injector blocks have to be repumped solid - a somewhat lengthy job.'

Saturday, August 1, was a maintenance day. A bracket was made and fitted to steady the steering column; the clutch was adjusted; the fuel tank was cleaned out; and the trap in the body floor, for access to adjust the clutch, was altered to be clear of the test load which sat over its original position. Lastly a box was fitted to hold tools and spares.

The great adventure began on Monday, August 3, with the anti-climax that had come to be expected. The adjustments to the clutch on the Saturday were found to have altered the pedal height and the rod fouled the boards of the cab floor, both of which had to be attended to before setting out for Bedford with Cyril Plane driving and Woolnough acting as mate. Cyril found it difficult to get the lever out of third gear, and the ammeter was found to be working erratically, but otherwise all went well. Distrusting the cleanliness of the fuel dispensed to the wagon he fitted a finer gauze to the filler in an endeavour to obviate the tedious routine with the filter and injector blocks.

The plan was to run two trips over the test route each day in opposite directions. This meant a 4 a.m. start! Thus Sunrising Hill and Fish Hill, the most taxing gradients on the route, were tackled alternately up and down. It was during the first descent of Sunrising that the interesting discovery was made that even with the wagon in first gear the combined effect of both hand and foot brakes fully applied could not bring it to a stand. Cyril Plane, who was driving, further noted that the hand brake was hard to apply. During the week some of the earlier troubles were run to ground and remedied. On the Tuesday, for instance, the clutch slip was traced to a leak of grease onto the Ferodo. The problem with third gear persisted. By the Wednesday two hands were needed on the gear lever to get the lorry out of third, and at Stratford-on-Avon that day it jammed immovably but mysteriously freed up when the gearbox cover was removed. Earlier in the day the generator had overheated and had had to be taken out of drive. The team's pleasure was made complete by the weights breaking off the governor fingers and fracturing the casing, covering the driver's feet with oil. After a temporary repair they were returning the lorry to Bedford when a nipple on the fuel pipe became unsoldered and they had to stop at a local garage to re-solder it before they could get back to Bedford. These problems meant a trip to Stamford the next day, Thursday, for repairs during which a fresh generator was put on and the governor was replaced. Work on the foot brake resulted in much better braking on the return trip.

Friday produced fresh troubles, the most tiresome of which was a sudden engine stoppage thought possibly to be due to a piston seizure. The engine was allowed to cool, was restarted, ran for about an hour, and repeated the performance. They drained the crankcase; found more of the mysterious fluff in the filter; filtered the oil; put it back and proceeded. No more stops happened but an unexplained engine knock developed, causing them to stop and examine the fuel system and to reprime the pumps. On Saturday the cause of the problems was found - a leaking copper asbestos washer in the fuel line was allowing air to be sucked in intermittently. A new washer cured both the involuntary stops and the knocking, and a full test circuit plus a shorter run to Stratford and back were completed. Despite their misfortunes the test crew had notched up 1092 miles in the week.

The next week began with two very satisfactory circuits on Sunday, August 9, with no problems except, perhaps, somewhat black exhaust. Monday, August 10, was wet. Seventy-five miles out from Bedford the engine ran No.3 big end and a new one was fitted on the road. Fluffy matter was found blocking the oil manifold outlet to No.3 splash tray. Despite this interruption two test circuits were done. For the Wednesday of that week the Aldwych House sales staff had arranged a further demonstration for the Campbell & Carter delegation by which it was hoped to reinforce the latter's favourable preliminary opinion. Tuesday was spent grooming the lorry for the task. Careful work by Storey on the fuel injection system produced a much cleaner exhaust. The next morning the lorry was driven sedately to Aldwych House where the delegates had been entertained by a posse of directors - Col. Garrett, Mr. E. Blackstone, Mr. James Howard, and Mr. W.J. Marshall. How all this party were carried on the lorry is not clear, but some may have followed by car. At 2.30 p.m. all set out for Hampstead. Apart from jumping out of third gear when climbing a gradient in the Finchley Road there was no untoward incident, and the visitors were again impressed, though they thought the noise and heat in the cab too much. Well pleased, the team took the lorry back to Bedford and did a single loop round the test route. All had a share in the driving that day - Burrows, Peecock, Cyril Plane, Harold Woolnough, and Bill Lankester.

On the Friday morning the lorry was driven over to the Dunlop factory at Fort Dunlop for an inspection to be made of the inner rear tyres, the centre treads of which were seen to be wearing in step fashion. The Dunlop inspectors pronounced this to be harmless. In the afternoon there was time for a run round the test route. All day the third gear gave trouble by jumping out. Having had a week with no engine trouble the crew were hopeful of a quiet Saturday but upon starting the engine that morning an ominous heavy knock came from cylinder No.4. It was opened up at once, and the turbulence block was found broken cleanly from the piston. The loose piece had got up behind the exhaust valve and jammed it, causing bending of the valve stem and a broken rocker arm. All were replaced though as there was no spare rocker arm Storey 'borrowed' one from the engine of the Garrett Blackstone tractor standing at Howard's works. After that the day went well, the drivers having mastered the technique of making silent gear changes, but at one point the gears again jammed though they freed off without dismantling. Periodic problems were experienced with the windscreen wiper. Some effort had been made on the Saturday morning to improve the working but with little real success.

The week which began on Sunday, August 16, was probably the worst up to that time. The first run of the day was about half a mile from Bedford when the engine began firing on only five cylinders. An exhaust valve spring pin collar had sheared, allowing the valve to remain open. After this had been put right the second run was made. This time the lorry and crew were 36 miles from Bedford when trouble hit them. A knock began which worsened until they could not go on. Jack Plane was sent for from Blackstones. The problem was again failure of the governor, with the additional complication that the intermediate gear which meshed with the timing wheel had broken as well. The big ends and injector blocks were examined to make sure there was no trouble there. All this was done on the road, and work went on throughout the night. Under Jack Plane's guidance a temporary repair was made which enabled the lorry to be driven very slowly to Stamford, arriving there in late evening. The batteries, run down by the use of the inspection lamp the previous night and by a defect which had occurred in the charging circuit, were put on charge but beyond that the test crew declined to go, not having been to bed for some forty-two hours. Next morning a new governor, in which Blackstones had drilled the weights to lighten them, was fitted. As a result the engine speed 'hunted'. Whilst the lorry was still in the works the aluminium ring positioning the starter motor on the flywheel housing broke in three places and had to be replaced. The charging problem was cured by fitting a new driving disc in the dynamo coupling. With all this work completed the company returned to Bedford.

The next day, Wednesday, was little better. On the first trip the lorry jibbed on Sunrising Hill, and after much bother the problem was tracked down to a hairline crack in a solder joint to a nipple in the fuel line. Peecock expostulated in his report 'All fuel pipe connections must be *brazed*.' No second run was made, but two were made the next day, the first without untoward events. On the second trip the engine overheated, something it had not done before, upsetting the tappet settings which had to be re-done on the road. This trouble did not recur in the cool of the day during the morning run on the Friday, though for good measure both top and third gears repeatedly stuck in mesh, and the hand brake had to be adjusted. As the day got hotter overheating trouble returned. The cause was found to be grease that had entered the cooling system through the impeller end bearing of the circulating pump. Seldom defeated, Peecock bought sufficient quantities of washing soda to fill the cooling system several times with a strong soda solution. Running the engine brought it to the boil, and each successive dosage was then drained off and renewed. By this means much grease was got rid of. After that a slow return to Bedford was attempted but on the way the exhaust valve in the third cylinder from the front had to be removed as it was in a bad state with nearly a third of the head melted away. They managed to finish the journey on four cylinders 'with a terrible exhaust'.

Before attempting any runs on the Saturday the sump was taken off to see what damage there might be in the crankcase. One big end bearing had run out, for a reason not apparent, and it was replaced. One compression was weak, and in removing the valve the cast iron valve box was broken being, in Peecock's estimation, 'a weak design'. Some worn cotters on the valve stems were replaced. On a short trial run the engine was still not running correctly. The piston which had been fractured and renewed the previous week was drawn and this time the turbulence block was found to be *burnt* away. The turbulence plate was likewise damaged. Baffled, Jack Plane and Peecock decided to go over to Stamford the next day, (Sunday, August 23) to see Frank Carter, taking the burnt piston and the injector block from the cylinder.

Having found him at home on the Sunday morning, they all went over to the works. First they tested the injector block and found it perfect so it was dismissed as a contribution to the troubles. Plane and Peecock returned to Bedford and fitted a new piston, having first to turn off part of the turbulence block so as to clear the distorted hole in the turbulence plate, preferring to leave work to the plate itself until the lorry went to Stamford for inspection, since it involved removing and replacing the water and exhaust manifolds. When the engine was started No.1 piston was found to be touching the turbulence plate, so next day the first job was to remove it and file it down. Hardly had the engine been reassembled and started than another big end bearing ran out. The cause of the trouble was eventually traced to a fractured Woodruff key that secured the drive gear to the pump shaft. This made the pump work only intermittently resulting at intervals in the loss of oil supply to the big ends. The test load was removed and left with Howards, after which the lorry limped home to Leiston on five cylinders.

At this point the Board must collectively have buried its head in its hands or, at least, the survivors must have done so as only Arthur Leggett and Richard Cheadle were left of the five who had launched the venture so hopefully ten months before, the others having fallen to the relentless economy axe. However, whilst the trials of No.35455 had been in progress the second and third chassis of the projected four (given the Nos.35470 and 35471) had been brought forward. The second of these was the petrol engined version, with the Meadows 6EX engine, for the 7/8 ton payload. Work on these two lorries continued and it seems that the engine was taken out of 35455 to be sent back to Blackstones at Stamford. In its place a fresh engine was sent in which, it was hoped, the defects of the original were eliminated. Whether or not it was entirely new or simply an extensive rebuild was not clear to the Leiston personnel at the time, nor can it be determined now, but, whether all or only part was new, in effect it was a different engine. It had been intended that the lorry should appear at the 1931 Commercial Motor Show, from November 5 to 14, and it was indeed entered, but in the event it did not go. Instead No.35470, complete but untried, was sent.

Apart from the fact that the chassis was under braked it had performed reasonably well, all major problems having arisen with the engine. So far as the brakes were concerned it was established early on in the programme of testing that they were less than adequate. The best stopping distances obtained at 30 m.p.h. to rest were:

Hand brake only	220 feet
Foot brake only	208 feet
Hand + foot brake together	125 feet

Even by the standards of 1931 these called for improvement, and the use of Servo assistance was proposed by Peecock to provide a remedy, if and when the lorry came to be put into production.

The problems with the engine, however, were fundamental. Despite all the efforts of Frank Carter and the Blackstone drawing office satisfactory performance in a lorry with the B.H.V.6 was never achieved, but in the Autumn of 1931 hope, officially at least, had not been abandoned. The new engine came from Blackstones and was fitted on October 22. It had force feed lubrication to the valve gear and injector block levers; a new design of pistons and turbulence plates so that the latter were a loose fit in the lever spigots, and there was more clearance in the holes round the turbulence block on the piston. Test runs over local roads began at once and went on until the end of the month, broken only by a trip to Stamford on October 28 to show Carter how dark the exhaust was and the amount of oil lost from the force feed system. Whilst it was at Stamford a new camshaft that had been made for it was fitted and the jets were altered. In the course of this work an undrilled oilway was found in the governor, calculated to have caused excessive pressure and, hence, the oil leaks. Work on these changes continued all night in preparation for the return to Leiston next day. In the haste, six set screws in the crankcase were left finger tight so that they eventually fell out and allowed the oil to escape. This happened at 3.45 a.m. on October 31 on a test run through Manningtree with the result that yet another big end bearing was lost. The crew had had much practice with this repair and it was accomplished almost with ease. Quite rightly, Peecock fulminated that studs, nuts, and lock nuts should have been used in the first place.

In anticipation of the arrival of the new engine the worm ratio on the rear axle had been altered from 7.75:1 to 6.25:1, and this change, taken in conjunction with a rather better performance from the engine, raised the road speed capability to a quite illegal 28 - 30 m.p.h., though contrariwise it meant that the lorry was no longer capable of drawing a trailer nor, when loaded to 6¼ tons, of climbing more than 1 in 6.5. Also, about this time, the crew had removed five out of the six plates in the silencer. Cyril Plane wrote a memorandum concerning this and one or two other points on November 18, 1931, just before he left for New Zealand with the Garrett 'All-Steel' thresher. In it he commented that the vandalism to the silencer had an almost imperceptible effect upon the noise but produced a marked improvement in the colour of the exhaust. He noted further that the engine covers on the driver's side of the cab had been covered with felt that had produced considerable abatement of cab noise but made it rather warm. He suggested an opening roof light in the cab to allow better ventilation, and bigger louvres in the external engine covers. He also disclosed that the turning circle to left and right were unequal. That to the right was 61' 0" diameter whilst the other was 62' 0". He further observed that the driver's feet would be less prone to slipping off the pedals if the pads had been made chequer plate pattern rather than decorated with the RG&S logo.

On November 1, the lorry, having otherwise behaved itself quite well, was sent back to Bedford to resume its reliability trials. On this run of 110 miles it averaged 9.9 miles per gallon. Frank Carter met it there with some spare parts for the engine 'in case they were required'. They soon were. On November 3 the engine began to miss on one cylinder as soon as it warmed up, and this trouble recurred next morning. Storey and Peecock eventually traced the cause to the injector valve sticking up on that cylinder. After they had eased it the trouble seemed to be cured and Burrows took the lorry out over the circuit, only to report on his return that it was missing badly and that, moreover, there was a loud engine knock when taking left-hand bends. In spite of having worked until the early hours of that day on the previous repair, Storey and Peecock immediately took down all the injection blocks, removed and eased the injector valves, reassembled the engine and took the lorry for a twenty mile run, over which it seemed satisfactory. They finished at 2.30 a.m. on November 5, leaving the lorry ready for Fred McKeer to take out at 4 a.m. At 8.30 he rang in to report a breakdown. Peecock and Storey went out by car to it to find that the fan pulley had come loose as a result of the thread stripping on the end of the crankshaft. By that time Fred had made a good temporary repair and the trip continued. Burrows took it out on the afternoon run and rang in to say that there was a bad knock again and that flames were issuing from the exhaust - after all, it was November 5! He eventually coaxed the lorry home, and to add to his pleasures he had had a puncture and had to change the wheel on his own. Meanwhile Storey had phoned Stamford and had been told to get the lorry there by 8.30 a.m. the next morning for examination.

The state of the engine made it quite impossible to get the lorry to Stamford the next day. By working much of the night they had pinned down the trouble to No.6 piston head having been burned away, burning the exhaust valve and valve seat at the same time. There was also a leak allowing fuel to enter the exhaust system. Peecock and Storey, therefore, went to Stamford in Peecock's car, leaving Burrows and Jimmy Drane, a Leiston fitter who had been seconded to the team, to dismantle the engine while they were away in order to get out the damaged piston and to take off the cylinder head. Whilst Peecock and Storey were at Stamford a cylinder head and exhaust valve in the same state as theirs arrived from another customer!

Work on the engine went on continuously, doubtless taxing the cheerfulness even of the irrepressible Jimmy Drane, and was completed late in the evening of Saturday, November 7. An immediate trial trip started off at 2 a.m. on the 8th, and the lorry returned from this without incident, but on the second lap that day it failed at Stratford. Peecock noted with feeling in his log: 'Am just going out with Storey to investigate. 8.0 p.m. on Sunday.' Worse was to come. They worked all that night to be rewarded at its conclusion by very poor running; more missing; a fuel line air lock, and the fan pulley loose again. On

November 11 he and Storey took the lorry to Stamford, the last seven miles running on four cylinders only. Wholesale problems were found including a major crack in the crankcase. The lorry was left at Stamford, and the whole team returned to Leiston.

By November 18 the engine had been so completely rebuilt as to be virtually new and was tried on the Stamford Works test bed, the trial extending over nearly a month during which many of the old problems recurred and were put right by Blackstones. On December 15 the test circuits from Bedford were resumed with rather better results than in the preceding series, though still dogged by silly imperfections such as, on December 30, yet another failure of the fuel oil pump gear wheel which had already been replaced three times (on November 19, 25, and 28) whilst the engine was still on the test bed at Stamford. Nevertheless, by January 5, 1932, a total of 5000 miles had been reached with the engine. At this mileage the exhaust had again become very dirty and the engine was not pulling well. Performance, particularly miles per gallon, continued to deteriorate. This 5000 miles taken with the mileage achieved in the first series of tests meant that the lorry had accomplished the 10000 miles laid down in the production plan and it was, therefore, taken back to Leiston.

On January 9, having been again repaired, it was loaded with a tractor and sent off to Temple Normanton, returning on January 11 to Stamford where, once again, new injection blocks were fitted in an endeavour to improve the mileage per gallon, which had been poor. On the outward trip the lorry had covered the 183 miles between Leiston and Mansfield at an average speed of 25 m.p.h. but at the expense of a consumption of about 8.8 m.p.g. After a few short trial runs with the new blocks and a return trip to Bedford the lorry left Stamford again on January 14 to pick up the tractor with the intention of getting back to Leiston on January 15. During the return trip from Yorkshire, at 11.30 a.m., a big end failed seven miles north of Stamford. A repair was made on the road, but because there was also a bad knock in the engine it was decided to halt overnight at Stamford for repairs. It was 7 p.m. by the time they got to Blackstone's works but by mid-day on Saturday the repair was done, and the party returned to Leiston that evening. After this experience, trials with No.35455 seem to have been abandoned, without any attempt having been made to carry out the simulated trunk journeys.

During the weeks when these events had been in progress test runs had been done with the petrol engined lorry which had gone reasonably well except that the petrol consumption figure was 4 miles per gallon. As a standard of comparison the firm took some readings from a Leyland Bull owned by Harber Brothers of Swanley, Kent, who knew the firm well because they ran Garrett undertypes. These showed that with perhaps rather larger loads, usually 8 to 9 tons, the Leyland was showing figures of something like 8 miles to the gallon. Various adjustments were made to the Zenith carburettor jets and air inlets in consultation with Meadows, all resulting in little improvement. Early in December, 1931, Fred McKeer drove the lorry to Meadows' works at Wolverhampton where, by a series of adjustments, the mileage figure was coaxed up to 7.64 m.p.g. There was talk of changing the Zenith for an S.U. carburettor, but whether or not this was done I do not know. Early in 1932 the third lorry (No.35470) seems to have been fitted with an Aveling & Porter engine for trials. Not much survives of its trial records but a note from Peecock records that on January 31 there was trouble caused by the nozzle valves of three of the cylinders sticking up. These were eased and the wagon performed well on the following day, covering 236 miles. Peecock noted that it ran well and that the exhaust was good. At that point it had evidently been on test for some time as he added a note 'Miles per gallon 10.15 for the last 600 miles'. The last run to be recorded was on January 24, the records of which existed when I wrote *Garretts of Leiston* but seem to have vanished when the Works was finally cleared.

Whilst the adventures with the six cylindered diesel lorry had been going on ,another venture had been in progress which, had it been rewarded with success, might have been very important to the future of the Works. In the Spring of 1931 an order had been obtained from Glasgow Corporation Cleansing Department for a diesel engined version of the Glasgow GTZ refuse collector. What prompted the Glasgow authorities to order it is not known to the author - perhaps to extend the working range beyond that of the already successful electric GTZ's. As to its general configuration the vehicle closely resembled the electrics from which its design was derived, although by necessity the cab was somewhat amended. The drawing work was in the Drawing Office roughly at the same time as the formative stages of the design of the four new internal combustion chassis, and it was in the designing of the diesel GTZ rather than in that of the lorries that one of the battles of principle was fought out. The Leggetts, father and son, were firmly of the belief that the engine ought to be carried in a sub-frame but the consensus of feeling

112

amongst the design staff was that to use this method of mounting caused an addition to the unladen weight, not justified by the benefits claimed to arise from its adoption. Since Arthur Leggett was a director his view prevailed in the case of the GTZ with the result that not only was the front axle loading increased but also that the engine was mounted much higher above road level than it otherwise need have been.

Work in the shops commenced on June 26, 1931. Despite being forward looking in its choice of prime mover it was, nevertheless, solid tyred and, unlike the GB6 and GM6, the cab was not fully enclosed, though the glazing that it contained was done with safety glass. The abridged specification of it that appeared in the order book was as follows:

> Special Glasgow type 'Garrett' diesel collecting vehicle, of special lowloading line. Equipped with Blackstone 4-cylinder vertical high speed heavy oil engine of 36-40 BHP with 12 volt CAV electric starting, radiator and bonnet, gearbox for four forward speeds and one reverse. Multi dry plate clutch. Vehicle mounted on cast steel wheels with solid rubber tyres 180mm for 670mm singles in front, and 140mm for 670mm twins at rear. Pressed steel frame with underslung springs. Cardan shaft drive; worm driven rear axle; forward type steering, and front mudguards.
> Two independent sets of internal expanding brakes - one foot and one hand operated - both acting on rear wheels. 20 gallon fuel tank fitted under nearside seat in cab. Semi-enclosed driver's cab constructed of steel, and extended to full width of body. Fitted with *Protectoglass* safety glass windscreen. Special all-steel side tipping body of 14½ cu.yd. capacity, with covered sheet steel top. Rail on roof. Rubber side curtains for dustless loading and additional side doors to each compartment. Bulkhead lamp fitted inside vehicle at front end. Instrument board mounted on steering column, equipped with ammeter, oil pressure gauge, plug and socket for inspection lamp, starting switches and panel illuminating lamp, and speedometer. Electric lighting set with 2 driving lamps fitted with dimming device, 2 loading lamps and one tail lamp; bulb horn; electric windscreen wiper; 2 basket carriers; one adjustable driving mirror, and complete with full outfit of tools and accessories.   No.35466   £1250 . 0 . 0

Despite the fact that the completed vehicle was effectively a prototype it was subjected only to relatively perfunctory road runs round the 20 mile circuit used for testing the steam wagons. It came through these without problems, was given the Works No.35466, and was sent off by rail to Glasgow on January 20, 1932. The conditions under which it was to work were, of course, much less demanding than those which were envisaged for the lorries, but it is believed that after a short life the engine unit was replaced by a Gardner. More importantly from the point of view of its makers and their successors there were no further orders for similar vehicles.

The affairs of the AGE group were by that time in a pitiful state. Edward Barford had detected Rowland in actions that, at best, could only be described as sharp practice and, at worst, totally dishonest. This has all been narrated in *Garrett 200* and need not be gone over again. By early 1932 the only executive director left at Leiston was Richard Cheadle and large scale dismissals had been made, both on the shop floor and in the administration. Finally on February 15 the axe fell and the Works was closed, Barclays Bank having secured the appointment of a Receiver. Thus all of those who had worked so hard on the lorry venture found themselves out of work. I do not know the subsequent personal histories of all of them but a few notes may be of interest. Jack Plane's sojourn at Blackstones had made him very expert on diesels. He subsequently emigrated to Johannesburg where he founded J.H.Plane & Co. Ltd. to trade in machinery, importing, *inter alia,* Gardner diesel engines, and ultimately became a millionaire. Cyril, after working along with his father for the successor company, later joined his brother in South Africa, becoming a director of Jack's firm. After a spell on the dole, Messrs. McKeer, Woolnough, Burrows, Drane, and Lankester were all re-employed by the new owners of the Works. Later still, Fred McKeer held a senior post in the service department at Mercedes-Benz (Great Britain) Ltd., Bill Lankester became a publican and Jimmy Drane an insurance agent. What happened to Peecock, in many ways the dominant figure, is not known.

The lorries were sold by the Receiver, the engines having been removed and returned to their manufacturers. Nos.35470 and 35471 were sold to Martin & Sillett Ltd. of Strood, Kent, for £550 the pair. Rumour says that their purchasers fitted them with Gardner engines and that they ran until Martin & Sillett themselves became insolvent in the late 1930's. The Leiston books give two accounts of what happened to No.35455. In one place it is mentioned as having been sold, complete with Blackstone engine, to Alf Cork & Son in Manchester for £550. In another it is said to have been sold, fitted with an Aveling & Porter engine, to John Sadd & Sons Ltd. for £355. The first is the truth, the second entry having arisen from confusion with a diesel-engined industrial tractor sold to Sadds.

After Beyer Peacock & Co. Ltd. had taken over the Works attempts were made to market a diesel lorry based on the GB6 but with a Gardner 5LW in it. This would have made it an excellent vehicle. On November 16, 1932, they sent a quotation to a Mr. J.Adams at a Post Office box number in Perth, Western Australia, for the supply of such a lorry at £1392 loaded onto rail at Leiston, offering alternatively to fit a 6LW engine for an additional £105. No lorries thus equipped were ever sold. Indeed it is questionable whether a sufficiently sustained effort was mounted to sell them or even whether Beyer Peacock were seriously interested in conducting it. Beyer Peacock themselves obtained a high proportion of their locomotive building work by being invited by consulting engineers or railway administrations to submit tenders. Though this may have required salesmanship of a fairly muted style conducted in a gentlemanly manner in an ambience such as the St.Stephen's Club, an effort to market lorries would have required an altogether more aggressive and extrovert approach which to the best of my knowledge was never attempted. Probably the nearest Leiston Works got to this under Beyer Peacock ownership was in the Friday night entertainments of Colin McFarlane, the Glasgow Cleansing Superintendent, by Bambrough or Reg King, though these were more cosy evenings with old friends than 'hard sell' encounters.

Fig.125. No.35455 in the Royal blue livery in which it appeared at the 1931 Commercial Motor Show. It was never registered whilst in Richard Garrett & Sons' ownership, carrying trade plates when on the road.

Fig.126. (below). This was the photograph posed for the sales brochure on the GB6, but actually shows No.35470. The scene is in Westward Ho, Leiston, opposite the railway goods shed.

Fig.127. A three quarter rear view of the same vehicle.

Fig.128. The full-face view of No.35470. There were differences in the scuttle, and no badge on the radiator. The registration number was 'borrowed' from steam wagon No.35206.

Chapter 8

... and the Conclusion of the Matter?

After a false start with the three early undertypes, wagon building went well with the 3 and 5-ton overtypes, though it never overtook that of Fodens. In 1919 the company began to build electric wagons - clean, quiet vehicles suited to town use. Soon afterwards steam wagon production switched to the modernised undertype, with free steaming boilers and extensive use of roller bearings. In the mid-1920's efforts began to enter the motor lorry market and to build diesel tractors. All these decisions seemed commercially and practically right. Why was the outcome - at least post 1919 - so disappointing?

Before attempting to answer that question it should, perhaps, be said that despite the sales of the 3 and 5-ton overtypes having lagged behind those of the Foden, they were satisfactory wagons in their own right with a performance that left behind such competitors as the Aveling & Porter, Burrell, Clayton, Tasker, and Wallis & Steevens. Though there had been problems before 1914 - for, after all, few human enterprises can avoid a sprinkling of them - the way in which fate seemed to play cat and mouse with the company began with the first World War. Until then the mainstay of the Garrett finances had been the portable engine and the threshing machine, both made and exported in large numbers. In 1913, the last full year before hostilities, the Works produced 543 portable engines and 424 threshers and similar machines. In 1919 the comparable figures were 159 and 46 respectively, whilst by 1927 they were 37 and 76. Thus between 80 and 90% of this trade had been lost and, with it, the basic income strength of the firm. Some of the trade was lost in the Austro-Hungarian empire, ruined in the struggle and dismembered by rampant nationalism after it. Much had been lost in Russia, brought to its knees by the War and the ensuing internal revolution. This latter brought with it the concomitant misfortune that the debt created by the monies and stocks detained in Russia by the Tsarist regime at the outbreak of war was repudiated by the new Soviet government. In other markets shortages and restrictions had made it impossible to supply goods during the war years, creating irreversible shifts of alliance in overseas customers towards American suppliers.

The War had struck, too, at the owning family and the Board of Directors. Carl Remy, the German director responsible for the trade with Continental Europe and long-time friend and confidant of Frank Garrett Senior, was lost to the firm. Frank Garrett Senior died of natural causes during the War and Stephen was killed in action. Alfred Garrett, always of a retiring disposition, lost his wife in tragic circumstances and, as a result, withdrew even further into himself. Frank Garrett Junior, discharged form the Army in 1915 as a Lieutenant Colonel, thus had board-room matters pretty much to himself, supported but never questioned by Alfred, and given practical assistance by the only other director, W.J.Marshall. He thus had the opportunity to ride hobby-horses, though this changed a little when his youngest brother, Victor, was invited onto the Board in 1917.

Government contracts that had kept the level of production high until 1918 collapsed abruptly at the Armistice. Though home demand for steam tractors and overtype wagons sustained the flagging output during 1919, sales of portables and threshers remained at a very low ebb. At the time the War broke out the firm had been in the closing stages of building the Top (or Station) Works. This had been used for war production and needed re-equipping for peace-time manufactures, whilst rearrangements and new machines were required in the Town Works. Besides the loss of his brother Colonel Garrett also had to come to terms with the death or disabling of many of the fittest and ablest younger men of the Works and town as a result of military service. Furthermore, from the stretched liquidity of the firm the monies had had to be found to fund the provisions of his father's will. It is easy, therefore, to see how, daunted by the problems with which he was confronted, he became attracted to the idea conceived by Thomas Aveling and Archibald Maconochie of combining all or most of the British agricultural engineering firms who found themselves similarly placed, thereby reducing home competition and, at the same time, creating a unit large enough to stand up to the North American firms. Thus was the notion of Agricultural & General Engineers born. AGE was not so much a disease in itself as a symptom. Quite apart from the prospect it held out of ameliorating the problems by which the Works was beset it appealed to his love of the grand gesture. Victor once confided to me that in his personal make-up his eldest brother had much more in him of the aristocratic Crofts from whom his mother was descended rather than of the line of

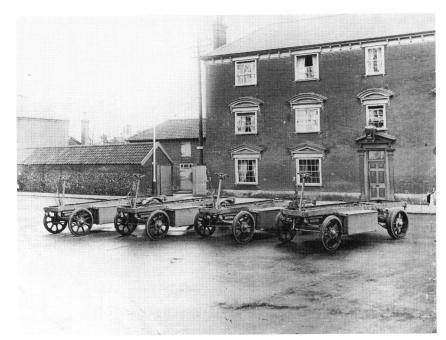

Fig.129. In 1920 no doubts assailed the Garretts about their position in Leiston. When they wanted Charles Clarke to photograph four chassis they occupied the whole of the public road (the present B1125) in front of the White Horse Hotel *for the occasion.* [S.R.O.]

Fig.130. Canterbury City Council bought No.161, primarily for refuse collection, in September, 1921. After they had used it for nine years they sold it to Hackney Borough Council who continued to use it for another decade. [S.R.O.]

Fig.131. Besides its duties as a dust cart No.161 had to act as a street watering wagon for which purpose it was provided with the tank body shown here, interchangeable with the tipper bodywork. [S.R.O.]

117

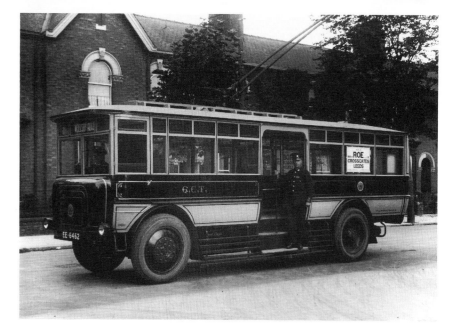

Fig.132. No.301 newly completed for Grimsby Corporation, late Summer, 1926. [S.R.O.]

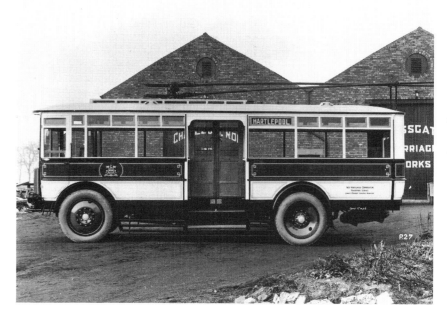

Fig.133. No.312, the first of the twelve cars for West Hartlepool, outside the Chas. Roe works at Crossgates, January, 1927. [S.R.O.]

Fig.134. Just delivered to Bradford in October, 1926, with Roe's sticker still in an offside rear window, No.297 shows how the body details were amended, in this case in the upper lights, to suit individual customers. [S.R.O.]

Suffolk blacksmiths in the Garrett ancestry. Frank, a thoroughly honourable man himself, was reluctant to suspect lack of integrity in those with whom these matters thrust him into contact. Besides this, not being rooted in practical engineering, as his Grandfather and Uncle Richard had been, he was thus much more susceptible to persuasive propositions. Richard had worked in the shops of the firm from the age of fourteen; had fought and punched his way amidst other lads; had sweated over recalcitrant machines; and grappled with problems of design. This made him always his own man. Col. Garrett, on the other hand, tended to see things from the bridge rather than the deck, and relied upon his salaried staff to transact matters of engineering for him, and upon the shrewd judgements of Frank Walker as to how well they had performed.

So far as the finances were concerned Teddy Ballam, the United Kingdom sales manager of Garretts, who was very close to the business circles in Ipswich, once assured Victor that, such was the esteem in which Garretts were held in Ipswich and East Suffolk, he would have been able, given the opportunity, to raise enough new capital in Ipswich alone to re-finance the Works. The more grandiose conception of AGE, however, had greater appeal and won the day. Frank Garrett joined Thomas Aveling as an enthusiastic promoter of the new combine. The brief post-war flush of demand for engines and machines for civilian use combined with the heady atmosphere of company promotion led a number of well-known firms into AGE, though for diverse reasons some of the best stayed aloof and some were not invited. The curious way in which AGE was set up and managed has been narrated elsewhere and does not need to be reiterated here except to say that Archibald Maconochie, the first AGE chairman and the man mainly responsible for the 'nuts and bolts' of setting it up soon cashed his entrepreneurial shares and retired, only to die not long after. His successor, said to have been his nominee, was Gwilym Rowland, a tax accountant, capable in his own field, probably out of his depth in questions of engineering but, nevertheless, determined to rule and maintain his own position by whatever means were needed. At boardroom level setting up AGE did nothing effective, as it ought to have done, to lessen the costs of the constituent companies. Instead each retained a full board of directors whilst AGE saddled the group with the burden of a pretentious London head office, a group board of directors, and a highly remunerated chairman.

A large and expensive selling organisation, which the companies did not need and could not afford, was set up at the new London headquarters and soon began to meddle in the design of the QL wagons with the results we have already seen in Part 2. Work on electric vehicles was already in hand at Leiston when AGE came into being but the expense of head office selling seriously prejudiced the overall cost whilst the tactics of the salesmen in getting orders by exaggerating the vehicles' capabilities led the firm into numerous problems of credibility, two of which were examined in detail in Chapters 2 and 3. During this period Garretts had considerable assets in the way of freeholds, buildings, machinery and stock in trade but remained chronically short of liquidity i.e. actual cash with which to pay wages and bills. Nevertheless, each month it was required to remit to head office a very substantial sum to cover the services performed by the group and the cost of maintaining the London establishment.

After the extravagance of central selling had been abolished as a consequence, in part, of the exposure by Melrose of the self deception involved in selling electric wagons at a figure below cost, revised instructions emanated from the AGE chairman that no product was to be sold at a figure less than that at which it could be made. This was all very well if applied with discretion, but when applied to prototypes it, in turn, became as absurd as the old selling system. It resulted in all kinds of development expenses being piled into the cost of the first example thus pushing its selling price too high. The idea was then developed that the cost department should calculate the cost spread over, say, a run of four - i.e. semi-scale. This brought down the unit cost but still left the prices high enough to discourage potential purchasers and thereby inhibit sales. This policy was at its height in the period 1926-28. In consequence, new models were thrust into quantity production to spread development costs over as many examples as possible and thereby massage the monthly returns to head office. The direst result of this policy was the rushing of the poppet valve engine and the 6-wheeled undertype wagon into production without the kind of punishing tests that were later used for the GB6 diesel lorry. Had such tests been allowed for both the new engine and for the 6-wheelers much subsequent embarrassment would have been avoided. Once relatively minor aberrations had been overcome both had the potential to be good products. Reaching that point whilst they were already being built and sold cost the firm not only a lot of money but also irrecoverable good will and credibility. The high price labels attached to the diesel tractors (see *Garrett Diesel Tractors*) and the unseemly struggles between the middle managements of the respective firms making engines and chassis demonstrate the workings of this system, as they argued, bickered, and prevaricated as to what prices they had tendered for components and what was to be charged to the buying public.

Nevertheless, living in the rocky depths of this unpromising AGE hierarchy must have been men of real perception, capable of recognising, ahead of most of the industry, the potential the diesel engine presented for use in agricultural tractors, dumpers, industrial locomotives, road rollers, and lorries. What went wrong was the way in which the curious fiscal policies of AGE caused their ideas to be put into practice. It was not until the GB6 lorry was attempted that it was at last realised that there was no cheap back door by which to enter the market, and that only by thorough trial and learning from mistakes could the venture be launched successfully. By then it was too late; the years of trying to implement new products on the cheap had eroded both the funds of the group and much of the goodwill attached to it. The tiresome practice of sales staff overlauding the characteristics of the vehicles, especially in the early days of the battery electrics, resulted in situations which were not only difficult, but expensive to retrieve. Sometimes, notwithstanding the spending of much money and effort on remedial work, the customer was still unhappy, though there were transactions where initial disappointment with a Garrett electric was overcome in a way that left the client pleased with his purchase. An illustration of this situation occurred with 2½-tonner No.105, mentioned in Chapter 3, delivered on September 20, 1919, to Siddall & Hilton Ltd., owners of the Standard Wire Co. at Sowerby Bridge, West Yorkshire. Every vehicle leaving their works had to climb a severe gradient, as steep as 1 in 4½ at its maximum, and the surrounding area abounded in steep hills on the public roads. The clients pointed this out when making their initial enquiry concerning the wagon but, nevertheless, were sent a standard vehicle with an Exide Ironclad battery of 198 ampere hours capacity and a 6 H.P. motor. Recalling the matter Raymond Siddall, the manager, wrote in 1925:

> After testing the vehicle was returned and in due course we received it back with a 258 ampere hour battery and 8 H.P. motor and sundry other little improvements. The suppliers of the vehicle meant to give us satisfaction and to prove that an electric would do the job. From that time (July, 1920) the vehicle has given us complete satisfaction.

This was a case where the sensible modifications carried out to the wagon to make it fit better into its working environment won back the goodwill of the client, but how much better it would have been for both parties, and how much less costly for Garretts, if a more realistic approach had been made by Sales in the first instance.

Why AGE should have been such a failure is harder to define. It was certainly not because Gwilym Rowland was a lazy or indolent man as even two of his sternest critics, Victor Garrett and Edward Barford, agreed that he was an indefatigable worker. Perhaps the prime reason for failure was that the motivation behind the merger was mistaken. The constituent companies were mainly family businesses temporarily in financially embarrassed circumstances. Their respective owners saw the amalgamation as a means of getting their own business out of a hole rather than as the foundation of a larger cohesive whole. Thus having united a series of firms that were a little shaky in their financial foundations the method the combined directorate adopted to stabilize them was not to underpin those dubious foundations but to build a lavish penthouse on the top. Each individual company continued to have its board of directors drawn from the family or from the pre-amalgamation directors, supplemented by technical directors nominated by AGE. Above these boards was the main board of AGE, the personnel of which consisted of the chairmen of the constituent company boards. Thus, in this respect, the economy that should have resulted from the amalgamation, viz. a reduction in the overall number of directors and in the salaries paid to them, was not achieved. Worse than that, the cost was actually *increased*. All this arose from Rowland's tactics for retaining absolute power in his own hands. The directors nominated by AGE depended upon him for their jobs so that he could, therefore, for his part reasonably expect them to back him. The directors drawn from the old owning families caused him a rather different problem of control. All, or most, were defensive as far as their position on their own boards and their 'own' works and workpeople were concerned. Doubtless they would have repudiated any suggestion that their relationship to the men on their respective works was feudal or patriarchal but, nevertheless, such was undoubtedly the case. Because of the way the main board was made up, Rowland was able to manipulate it by encouraging the formation of temporary cliques and alliances, where necessary fanning the guarded but never absent mutual suspicion the members developed one for another. It was of no consequence to him if they failed to act in concert so long as they never combined against him. When he believed himself to be threatened by a board member Rowland often succeeded in subduing the offender merely by his formidable personality. If this failed, he might, perhaps, isolate the transgressor by a process of innuendo, suggesting to board members whose voting intentions he could not rely upon that his opponent was a threat to them or to their family works, and that only by close support of the Chair could his (Rowland's) hand be strengthened sufficiently to avert the threat. In this way he kept his power intact until the final few days of the group.

Since the perennial problem Rowland faced was shortage of liquidity he was forced into using such monies as there were for purposes for which they were manifestly not intended. It also placed the companies deeper and deeper into debt to their bankers whilst at the same time leading on, as seen earlier, to neglect even of renewals that were needed to keep the factories water-tight. Nevertheless, the majority of the companies were fundamentally sound and after the AGE crash, most were revived either by new owners or by the erstwhile family owners, such as the Bentalls or the Paxmans, finding backers to buy back what had once been theirs. The basic assets were large and the pressing problem, therefore, came down to liquid cash and the indebtedness to the banks.

Bearing this in mind, one is tempted to ask the question 'Need the crash have happened?' When *Garretts of Leiston* was being written the late Sir Guy Hambling of Rookery Park, Yoxford, heard of our researches and invited us to see him one evening. His profession had been the law, and his father had been chairman of a clearing house bank. He had, moreover, known the Garretts. Thus on all counts he was well qualified to comment upon the events of February, 1932. 'Bankers are a panicky lot' he observed. 'A banker is like a man with a splendid umbrella. When the weather is fine he is more than willing to lend you his umbrella, but when the day comes that there is a storm of rain and thunder, he snatches back his umbrella.' The rain and thunder in 1932 was the onset of the Slump, the consequence of the disastrous financial collapse in the United States, and Sir Guy went on to say that had the banks to whom the AGE group owed money been less precipitate it might have been saved by a new chairman.

Almost exactly the same opinion was expressed by Edward Barford who had been instrumental in exposing Rowland's malpractices. Under a chairman who could have commanded the confidence of the creditors and a vigorous general manager, a part for which he undoubtedly cast himself, he believed the group could have been brought round, though the process would have been painful. He did, indeed, reinvigorate part of it as Aveling Barford, formed by joining together Aveling & Porter Ltd. and his own family firm of Barford & Perkins Ltd. on a fresh site at Grantham. Keeping the group together for perhaps another four or five years would have carried it past the end of the Slump, and would have seen it to the onset of the rearmament programme in which many of its constituents were well qualified to participate. Had it reached that point its survival would have been assured - not in perpetuity, perhaps, but at least until the woeful collapse of so much of the country's engineering capacity since 1970.

Had Leiston Works continued under Richard Garrett & Sons Ltd., work on the diesel lorry project would have gone on, too. A new and decisive group chairman could well have decreed a change in the source of the diesel engine to be employed, perhaps to Gardners (as the successor company did with the tractors) or, who knows, to a perfected version of the Aveling Invicta engine brought to commercially viable form by Frank Perkins who, had there been no collapse, might not have set up his own manufacturing company. A Garrett diesel lorry thus developed might have shared the burgeoning market for such vehicles with firms like Foden and ERF. Victor Garrett, despite the fact that he often found himself in disagreement with the ideas and actions of his cousin, Edward Barford, once said to me 'Edward could have done it. He understood engineering, and was strong enough and ruthless enough to have completed the job.'

Fig.135. Artist's impression of a 4/5 ton low line vehicle for Birmingham. In spite of getting to the stage of a drawing list (No.385 of March 3, 1926) it still did not go ahead.

Fig.136. The GT No.311 (October 2, 1926) of Manchester Corporation Electricity Dept. decorated for a carnival.

Fig.137. One of the Lima cars in Jirón Punto c.1928. [Allen Morrison collection]

Fig.138. Trolley buses often superseded trams, but for a trolley bus to become a tram is, as far as I know, unique to Lima. The picture below shows one of the Lima cars used to rebody a tram. Taken October, 1946, in Jirón Carabaya. [Allen Morrison collection]

PARTICULARS OF TEST ON DYNAMOMETER.

	CURRENT. AMPS	VOLTS AT MOTOR	MOTOR SPEED R.P.M.	MOTOR TORQUE LBS. FT.	B.H.P CALCULATED FROM TORQUE & SPEED	H.P. INPUT	% EFFCY.
Commencement of 60 Hrs running	120	85	1010	42.2	8.13	13.7	59.3%
After running for 8 Hrs	122	84.5	1010	40.7	7.84	13.8	56.8%
" " " 15 hrs	125	81.5	910	46.4	8.05	13.65	59.4%
" " " 20½ hrs	116	85	950	41.2	7.46	13.2	56.6%
BRAKE BLOCKS LINED WITH FERODO → " " " 29 hrs	123	84	930	48.5	8.6	13.8	62.2%
" " " 36 hrs	120	84.5	1054	43.8	8.8	13.6	64.6%
" " " 47 hrs	121	85	1075	44.8	9.18	13.8	66.6%
" " " 55 hrs	124	84.5	972	52.5	9.72	14.05	69.1%
	121	84.5	1005	49	9.38	13.7	68.4%
" " " 60 hrs	115	85	1033	42.2	8.32	13.1	63.4%
	119	85	1033	46.4	9.14	13.57	67.4%
Run immediately after the 60 hrs running with 5 tons on bare chassis	127	86	1033	49.8	9.8	14.65	66%
	124	86	1033	50.4	9.96	14.3	69.5%
	125	86	1033	50.0	9.85	14.4	68.4%
As above but with Duckhams "Adcol" oil in rear axle to replace Vacuum "C" oil.	122	84.5	1055	45.8	9.2	13.8	66.6%
	121	84.5	1075	45.8	9.4	13.7	68.6%
	124	84.5	1033	49.0	9.65	14.0	68.8%

The volts (as above) have been corrected to give the actual reading at motor.

All tests, with the exception of the last two were run with one Ton of pig iron on the chassis; and all with the exception of the last with Vacuum "C" oil in rear axle case.

The efficiency, as given, includes losses in motor, propeller shaft, worm gear, & bearings and wheel bearings.

Fig.139. *The record sheet of a dynamometer test of the first Glasgow GTZ, No.324, carried out on January 8, 1927.* [the late H.R.Simpson]

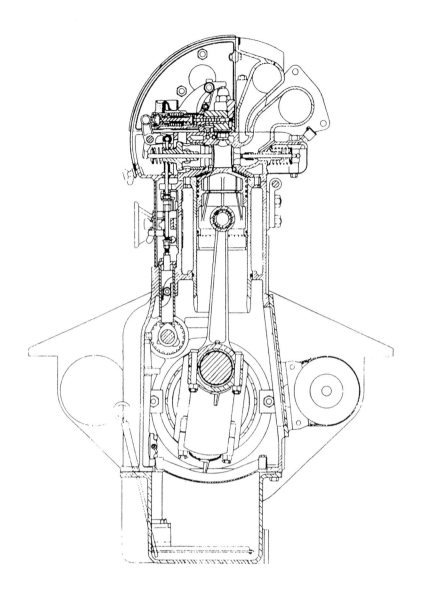

Fig.140. Cross section of the original Blackstone BHV6 engine used in the GB6 lorry, the much more successful four cylindered version of which was used in the Garrett diesel tractors. The fuel oil was carried in the passage at about 1 o'clock to the combustion chamber above the piston head.

Fig.141. The operation of the Garrett trolley buses began in Ipswich and ended there. Here is No.21 (Works No.273), still on solid tyres, in St.Matthews St., Ipswich, in the late twenties. Post-war redevelopment swept away all the buildings on the left of the picture to make way for Civic Drive. [S.R.O.]

124

Report to the Directors of Messrs. RICHARD GARRETT & SONS Ltd
                          re: ELECTRIC VEHICLES   23rd December, 1919

The object of this report, and the investigations leading up to it, is to place clearly before the Directors the experience which we have so far obtained from the construction of Electric Vehicles, the actual facts as to the comparative merits of our competitors' Vehicles, and the technical and constructive improvements which we must carry out to enable us to produce the very best Vehicle on the market.

It is not suggested that the recommendations put forward in this report should in any way interfere with immediate mass production as obtained in our present Electric Vehicle Shop, but we are strongly of the opinion that every effort should be made to put these modified designs into operation by the time we are ready to undertake mass production in our new Shops at the Station Works.

The design and construction of an Electric Vehicle is a totally different proposition to any other form of road transport, and in order to make it a success certain fundamental characteristics of the factors affecting its efficiency must be thoroughly understood; further than this, although the commercial field to which we can supply electrics is very wide, the limits within which they can be worked successfully are very narrow, and it is of great importance indeed that these limits should be fully appreciated by our selling organization as an electric can be a great success under certain conditions and a dead failure under others.

It is proposed, in this report, to clearly define these limits for our future benefit.

When an Electric Vehicle is put to work, it should be so constructed that the greatest possible amount of the energy stored in its batteries can be used in doing useful work. Useful work is represented by mileage, so that road conditions being equal the criterion of efficiency for an Electric Vehicle is the number of ampere-hours per ton-mile. The mileage which can be obtained from an Electric Vehicle is governed by two very definite factors:-

a]   The road conditions under which it is worked.

b]   The efficiency of the Vehicle itself.

It is interesting to show the maximum mileage which could be obtained from Garrett Vehicles when working under ideal road conditions and with an efficiency of 100%. Ideal road conditions would be a perfectly level road of asphalt, tarmacadam or macadam surface, hard and dry; the following table shows the mileage which would be obtained:-

'GARRETT' Electrics under Ideal Conditions

Size of Vehicle	Capacity	Specified Speed	Total loaded Weight	H.P. exerted	AMP/HRS per mile
No.3	1½ tons	11 M/Hr.	T5. 5. 0.	3.86	2.97
No.4	2½ tons	10 M/Hr.	T6. 7. 0.	4.23	3.59
No.5	3½ tons	8 M/Hr.	T8. 5. 0.	4.40	4.67

Size of Vehicle	Capacity of Battery	Mileage on one charge	Average current	Battery Voltage
No.3	193 AMP/HRS	65	32.70 AMPS	88
No.4	193 AMP/HRS	54	35.90 AMPS	88
No.5	258 AMP/HRS	55	37.40 AMPS	88

The horse-power shown in the above table is calculated on the assumption that the road resistance per ton at the specified speed is 25 lbs. This figure is obtained by reference to well-known authorities on such matters and is also borne out by our own experiments on the roads; it is a figure such as would be obtained, for instance, on Blackpool Promenade in dry weather, or any other good city road.

The Mechanical losses in the Motor and Vehicle.

We know by actual experiment that the Garrett Vehicles, when running on a level road having a resistance of 25 lbs per ton, absorb the following currents:-

Size of Vehicle	Speed	Amps	Volts
No.3	11.75 M/Hr	51	86
No.4	10	52	86
No.5	8	57	86

Transferring these figures to the brake test curves of the two motors we have the following results:-

Electrical H.P.	Motor Efficiency	Motor B.H.P.	H.P. at road surfaces	Mech.Eff.power transmission	H.P. lost in transmission	AMP/HRS per mile	Mileage on one charge	Mileage specified in our quotation
5.87	80.00%	4.70	4.12	87.50%	.58	4.34	44.6	40 - 45
6.00	80.50%	4.82	4.23	87.80%	.59	5.20	37.10	35 - 40
6.45	77.00%	4.96	4.40	89.00%	.56	7.12	36.2	35.00

These tables bring out some very important results. They show the actual mileage that can be obtained on our Vehicles when used in good level roads; in actual practice owing to motor and transmission losses we are only getting in the case of the No.3 and No.4 Vehicles 69% of the available battery mileage and in the case of the No.5 Vehicle only 66%. The loss in power transmission is not unreasonable when it is remembered that one countershaft, three chains and four road wheels have to be turned round. If the present countershaft drive were replaced by the double motor drive direct on to the back wheels as in the Electromobile design, the transmission losses would be reduced; but <u>suppose</u> by so doing this transmission efficiency could be raised to 95% - and it would have to be a very beautiful construction to realize 95% efficiency in practice - the mileage capacity of the Vehicle would only be very slightly increased, the No.3 Vehicle doing 47.2 miles, the No.4 doing 39.5 miles, and the No.5 doing 38.9 miles. The biggest loss is in the motor which in all three cases wastes about 20% of the power which it receives. It must be clearly understood that the mileage figures given above only apply to a non-stop run on a good straight level road of which the road resistance does not exceed 25 lbs. per ton. If any stopping or starting takes place during this run, or any deviation from the straight thus bringing into operation the steering mechanism and the differential action of the countershaft the mileage will be slightly reduced.

Another noticeable point is that the No.3 Wagon is capable of attaining 11¾ miles per hour instead of 11 as shewn in our specifications.

Hill Climbing

When travelling up an incline the motor of an electric vehicle uses a much larger current than when travelling on the level. The great disadvantage of a series motor which we use is that its efficiency falls very rapidly after the current exceeds a certain amount. The efficiency of the 6 H.P. Motor is at its highest when the current lies between 51 and 125 amperes; at these two currents the efficiency is 80% and at 85 amperes the efficiency is 87%. If 125 amperes is exceeded the efficiency drops rapidly being 60% at 190 amperes and only 32% at 300 amperes. The efficiency of the 8 H.P. Motor is at its maximum when the current lies between 57 and 180 amperes being 77% at these two currents and 86% at 100 amperes. If 180 amperes is exceeded, the efficiency drops to 62% at 270 amperes and to 40% at 400 amperes. The following table shows the degree of incline and the mileage which can be obtained from our Vehicles provided that a current of 125 amperes is not exceeded in the case of the 6 H.P. Motor and 180 amperes for the 8 H.P. Motor:-

Size of Vehicle	Incline	Road Speed	Mileage on one charge	Average current	Amp/Hrs per mile	
No.3	1 in 32	7.10 M/hr	10.95 Miles	125 Amps	17.60	6 H.P. Motor
No.4	1 in 34.5	5.50 M/hr	8.50 Miles	125 Amps	22.70	6 H.P. Motor
No.5	1 in 20	4.38 M/hr	6.30 Miles	180 Amps	41.00	8 H.P. Motor

It is to be noted that these calculations are based on a road resistance of 25 lbs per ton, and the mileage given shows the length of an incline up which the vehicle would travel before the battery was exhausted. The actual mileage which the vehicle would have covered on returning to its starting point would be about double that shown in the above table, because it would travel up the incline until its battery was exhausted and would then return down the incline to its starting point under the force of gravity and without using power. It is of very great importance that we should all appreciate the effect of hill climbing has on the mileage of the vehicle. Take the case of a man who purchases a No.5 Vehicle which, on level roads, will do 36.2 miles per charge. If he climbs an incline of 1 in 20 and 3.15 miles long, his mileage per charge is reduced to 24.4 miles.

The Garrett Vehicle, will, of course, climb inclines far steeper than those specified above; they will probably go up 1 in 4 the only limit being the torque of the motor at low speeds and the consequent over-heating, but it is not economical that they should be put on inclines steeper than the above except for very short distances owing to the poor efficiency of the motors at heavy currents.

The Effect of Chassis Weight on Mileage

If the losses in the transmission gear and the motor are neglected, the increase in mileage on the level or on an incline is directly proportional to the reduction in weight of the loaded Vehicle; that is, if the weight is halved, the mileage is doubled. In actual practice the constant internal losses of the Vehicle somewhat reduce this proportion, but still leave the question of Chassis weight reduction of very great importance. To show this clearly the following tables give the percentage weights of the chassis, battery and load of the various Vehicles:-

Size of Vehicle	Total loaded weight	Chassis + Body without Battery	Battery alone	Load alone % total loaded wt.	Battery alone	Chassis alone
No.3	5.25 tons	2.975 tons	0.775 tons	28.60%	14.75%	56.65%
No.4	6.35 tons	3.075 tons	0.775 tons	39.40%	12.20%	48.40%
No.5	8.25 tons	3.560 tons	1.190 tons	42.40%	14.40%	43.20%

The No.3 comes out very heavy and one of our first jobs should be to re-design it and reduce its weight. At present it is practically the same weight as our No.4 Chassis; this is due of course to standardisation of parts. The weight of the Chassis should be reduced by at least ½ ton. With regard to the Nos. 4 and 5, a 10% reduction of Chassis weight would only mean about 4½% reduction of total weight and a 4½% better mileage, and for this slight improvement it seems hardly worth while to make the extensive structural alterations necessary.

Effect of Bad Roads

From the earlier sections of this report, there seems to be no doubt that the American Designers in the first instance when laying out their scheme of Electric vehicles only intended them for work on good city roads with a tractive resistance not exceeding 25 lbs per ton and inclines not exceeding 1 in 20.

The English Manufacturers have simply copied these designs as regards motor and battery capacity without realizing the efficient limits within which the Vehicle can be worked. If a Vehicle is kept on a level road, the roads would have to be very bad indeed before the motor was worked uneconomically. This is shown in the following table:-

Size of Vehicle	Road resistance lbs per ton	Road Speed	Mileage on one charge	Average current	Amp Hrs per mile	Motor
No.3	95	7.10 M/hr	10.95 Miles	125 Amp	17.60	6 H.P.
No.4	102	5.50 M/hr	8.50 Miles	125 Amp	22.70	6 H.P.
No.5	133	4.38 M/hr	6.30 Miles	180 Amp	41.00	8 H.P.

From the above it is seen that if a Vehicle is kept to level roads economical working can be obtained if the road resistance is as high as 100 lbs per ton; the mileage depending purely on battery capacity. This is of course a very bad road and such roads would never be met with in town work. the roads all over the country are in a very bad condition owing to neglect during the war; city roads during wet weather and in the winter months probably average a road resistance of about 50 lbs per ton and the vehicle should be designed to suit this. With a road resistance of 50 lbs per ton the steepness of the incline up which a vehicle would travel is considerably reduced as shown in the following table:-

HILL CLIMBING WITH A ROAD RESISTANCE OF 50 LBS PER TON

Size of Vehicle	Incline	Road Speed	Mileage on one charge	Average current	Amp Hrs per mile	Motor
No.3	1 in 50	7.10 M/hr	10.95 Miles	125 Amps	17.60	6 H.P.
No.4	1 in 51	5.50 M/hr	8.50 Miles	125 Amps	22.70	6 H.P,
No.5	1 in 24	4.38 M/hr	6.30 Miles	180 Amps	41.00	8 H.P.

From the foregoing it is possible to make the following definite decisions for economical working:-

a]   The maximum current on the No.3 and No.4 Vehicles when running must never exceed 125 amps except for very short periods and the average current used must not exceed 85 amps. Under these conditions the No.3 Vehicle uses 9.54 Amp.Hrs. per mile with a mileage of 20.3 and the No.4 Vehicle would use 12.25 Amp.Hrs per mile with a mileage of 15.8 per charge.

b]   The maximum current on the No.5 Vehicle when running must never exceed 180 amps except for very short periods, and the average current must not exceed 110 amps. Under these conditions the No.5 Vehicle would use 18.6 Amp.Hrs. per mile with a mileage of 13.9 per charge. The average speeds in the three cases would be No.3 - 8.92m/hr, No.4 - 6.94 m/hr, No.5 - 5.92 m/hr.

If the currents specified above are not exceeded the best possible is being obtained from the Vehicle and we cannot improve the mileage in any way except by increasing the battery capacity.

If a Vehicle is sold to work in very hilly districts and very bad roads calling for heavier currents than the above, a larger motor must be installed in order that it may work at the peak of its efficiency; in the case of the Nos.3 and 4 Vehicles, an 8 H.P. Motor must be used and a 10 H.P. Motor for the No.5 Vehicle.

In this connection we wish to impress upon the Directors the extreme importance of instituting a proper selling organization for this trade. The success of an electric vehicle absolutely depends up[on the conditions under which it is worked. Before an order is taken an intelligent study of the road conditions should be made by an expert from these Works who can judge inclines and road resistances; the size of the motor and battery can then be specified. If the conditions are such that an electric vehicle is not likely to give satisfaction we must not quote. One customer perhaps only wishes to institute a delivery service of 10 miles per day. Another customer may wish to do long non-stop journeys totalling 30 miles per day. All these factors must be taken into consideration; it is absolutely ridiculous to specify as we are now doing - a mileage of 35 to 40 miles on one charge on good level roads. This conveys no information to the customers and very probably misleads them.

Our Competitors Vehicles.

During the last few weeks we have had opportunities of examining under actual working conditions the following makes of Vehicles:-

1]   Ransomes 2½-ton Vehicle with double front wheel drive at Messrs Crittall's of Braintree.
2]   Ransomes 2½-ton Vehicle with double front wheel drive at E.R. & F.Turner's of Ipswich.
3]   G.V. 3½-ton Vehicle with countershaft drive and single Motor belonging to the Ipswich Corporation.
4]   G.V. 3½-ton Vehicle with countershaft drive and single Motor belonging to Mr. Tibbenham of Ipswich.
5]   G.V. 3½-ton Vehicle with countershaft drive and single Motor belonging to the Blackpool Cleansing Department.
6]   G.V. 2½-ton Vehicle with countershaft drive and single Motor belonging to the Blackpool Cleansing Department.
7]   Electromobile 2-ton Vehicle with double motor rear wheel drive belonging to the Blackpool Cleansing Department.
8]   Electromobile ½-ton Vehicle with I.M.V. Battery and Pneumatic Tyres on front wheels belonging to Boots Cash Chemists of Blackpool.
9]   Electromobile 1-ton, 2-ton, and 3½-ton Vehicles with I.M.V.5, 7, and 8 Batteries, belonging to the Blackpool Co-operative Society.
10]   Edison ½, 1½, and 2-ton Vehicles with Edison Batteries Nos.A4, A6, and A8; belonging to the Blackpool Co-operative Society.

Ransomes Vehicles, 2½-ton Size

1]   Crittall's of Braintree
         In Winter weather,   11.2 Amp/hrs per mile
                                              Load factor - 33%
                                              Battery capacity - 286 Amp/hrs
                                              Mileage on one charge - 20.1
         In Summer weather,   8.0 Amp/hrs per mile
                                              Load factor - 36%
                                              Mileage on one charge - 28.3
2]   E.R. & F. Turner of Ipswich
         In Winter months   12.3 Amp/hrs per mile
                                              Mileage on one charge - 28.3
         In Summer weather   10.6 Amp/hrs per mile
                                              Mileage on one charge - 24.1

Further light is thrown on the performance of the Ransome Vehicles by an article appearing in *The Commercial Motor* of December 23rd 1919, in which a run from Ipswich to London is recorded during Winter weather:-

A journey of 41 miles with 1½ tons   Amp/hrs per mile - 9.65
A journey of 36 miles running light   Amp/hrs per mile - 7.1
Without regeneration their figure will be at least 10% higher.

G.V. Vehicles
3]   Ipswich Corporation 3½-ton Size
In Summer weather   10.75 Amp/hrs per mile
4]   Tibbenham of Ipswich
In Summer weather   7.3 Amp/hrs per mile
The higher consumption of the Ipswich Corporation Vehicle is accounted for by the fact that it was employed for a portion of its daily work on heavy sandy roads.
5 & 6] Blackpool Cleansing Department 2½ and 3½ ton Size
When used for Summer Watering   6 to 7 Amp/hrs per mile
When used for refuse collecting   9 to 10 Amp/hrs per mile, rising to 11 to 12 Amp/hrs per mile in bad weather.

Electromobile
7]   Blackpool Cleansing Department 2-ton Size
In Winter weather   11.7 Amp/hrs per mile
In Summer weather   9.29 Amp/hrs per mile
8]   Boots Cash Chemists ½-ton Size
These people can get 45 miles per charge on Blackpool roads with an IMV5 Battery of 161 Amp/hrs capacity
9]   Boots Cash Chemists 1, 2, and 3½-ton Sizes
On Blackpool roads, any of these vehicles can do 30 miles per day on one charge.
Edison ½, 1½, and 2-ton Vehicles
10]   Boots Cash Chemists, Blackpool
The Edison Vehicles have given better service than the Electromobile, and especially the Edison Batteries.

It is interesting to compare the results obtained from Garrett Vehicles against the above:-
No.5 Garrett sold to Blackpool Corporation
In Winter weather   11 to 12.5 Amp/hrs per mile - giving a mileage of 22½ per charge.
(Detailed statistics of this wagon are given at the end of this report).
No.5 Garrett sold to G.E.R. at Ipswich, 4years old.
In Summer weather   10.6 Amp/hrs per mile
In Winter weather   11.5 Amp/hrs per mile

For the purposes of comparison, the following tables show the weights of various Electric Vehicles as manufactured in America:-

Size of Vehicle	Wt of Chassis only	Wt. of Battery only	Wt. of Body where known	Battery Capacity Amp/hrs	Specified Amp/hrs per mile	Specified miles per charge
Anderson Electric Car Co. with Edison Batteries						
½-ton	.8 ton	.362 ton		150	2.70	50
1 ton	1.18 ton	.535 ton		225	3.60	50
2 ton	1.93 ton	.715 ton		300	5.20	45
3½ ton	2.84 ton	1 ton		375	7.50	40
4½ ton	2.95 ton	1.20 ton		450	8.00	40
Baker Truck Co. with Edison Batteries						
3½ ton	2.78 ton	1 ton		375	5	40
Connecticut Truck Co.						
2 ton	1.41 ton	0.814 ton			4.14	45
3½ ton	2.16 ton	1.185 ton			6.10	53
G.V. Co. with Ironclad-Exide Battery						
3½ ton	3.42 ton	1.10 ton	0.71 ton	258	6.75	40
E.Walker with Ironclad-Exide Battery						
3½ ton	2.45 ton	1.19 ton	0.81 ton	258	7.90	35
Ward						
3½ ton	2.19 ton	0.87 ton	0.53 ton			32
Waverly						
3½ ton	2.71 ton	0.95 ton	0.71 ton		6.40	40-50

The weight of the Garrett 3½ ton Chassis without Battery or body is 3.05 tons which is much heavier than the same size American Machines with the exception of the G.V; this latter Chassis has, however, been lightened since it has been manufactured in England. Another interesting point is the much higher battery capacity of the American Machines.

Conclusions
1]   The current consumption and mileage on one charge of the Garrett Vehicles are about the same as on our Competitors Machines. This fact is definitely established.

2]   We do not therefore propose to make any alteration in design in the immediate future except such small modifications as may be suggested by the Works Department to aid in mass production.

3]   The exception to the above is the No.3 Vehicle. We must make an effort as soon as possible to reduce the weight of this Chassis by at least ½ ton.

4]   We think that if the selling price will permit, a larger size Battery should be fitted as standard in the No.4 and 5 Vehicles; the No.4 to have 226 Amp/hr capacity instead of 193, and the No.5 to have 290 Amp/hr capacity instead of 258.

5]   As pointed out before, we are strongly of opinion that the selling organization should be so arranged that expert knowledge can be brought to bear upon our Customers' requirements.

6]   It would be a great advantage to fit a high efficiency motor to our Vehicles as proposed by Mr. Waters of the Stowmarket Engineering Co. If this cannot be arranged, higher powered motors of the present type should be supplied in certain cases; and charged as an extra.

7]   We propose at an early date to carefully examine our present system of motor control and interlocked Brake Gear.

Fig.141. E-type chassis, No.391, showing the kerbside control applied on the near side. It was to have been sent to South Africa but the order was cancelled. Later it was renumbered 433 and sold to St. Albans.   [S.R.O.]

Fig.142. Table, taken from catalogue No.604, showing the sizes of refuse collecting bodies Garretts were prepared to supply.

SIZE.			
30-cwt.	4 cu. yds.	—	—
2-tons.	4½ cu. yds.	—	—
2½-tons.	5½ cu. yds.	6½ cu. yds.	—
3½-tons.	8 cu. yds.	9 cu. yds.	10 cu. yds.
5-tons.	11 cu. yds.	12 cu. yds.	13 cu. yds.
6-wheel.	15 cu. yds.	16 cu. yds.	—

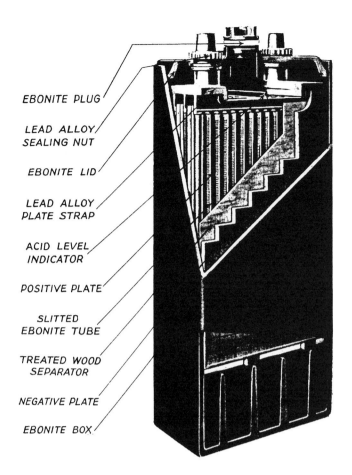

EBONITE PLUG

LEAD ALLOY
SEALING NUT

EBONITE LID

LEAD ALLOY
PLATE STRAP

ACID LEVEL
INDICATOR

POSITIVE PLATE

SLITTED
EBONITE TUBE

TREATED WOOD
SEPARATOR

NEGATIVE PLATE

EBONITE BOX

Fig.143. Cut-away drawing showing the construction of the Exide-Ironclad battery as used by Garretts.

Fig.144. The lead frame of an Exide negative plate.

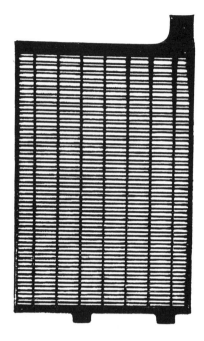

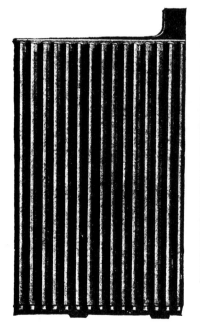

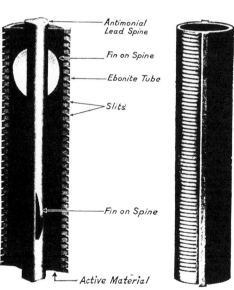

Antimonial
Lead Spine

Fin on Spine

Ebonite Tube

Slits

Fin on Spine

Active Material

Fig.145. (left) The Exide positive plate, with details of the slit ebonite tube and the lead spine rod, with a view of the external aspect of the ebonite tube.

Fig.146. (below) Horizontal plan of part of an Exide cell showing how the components fitted one to another.

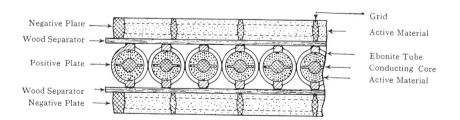

Negative Plate

Wood Separator

Positive Plate

Wood Separator
Negative Plate

Grid
Active Material

Ebonite Tube
Conducting Core
Active Material

APPENDIX 2   Batteries

The essential ingredient and, simultaneously, the greatest weakness of the independent electric vehicle is its battery or, more properly, accumulator. The electrical capacity of the battery determines the vehicle's range, working time between charges, and load carrying ability, from which has to be deducted, of course, the very considerable weight of the battery itself. Even if I had the specialised knowledge, this is not the place for a lengthy dissertation upon batteries, but these were so critical a part of the electric vehicle story that a brief mention is called for. Traction batteries are of secondary type. Unlike primary cells they do not actually generate the current available from them but provide the means of storing an electrical charge to be used later. In a word, they are akin to storage tanks for electricity. The early direct current stations, generating for public supply, had large battery rooms enabling current generated at their off-peak periods - at that time the daylight hours - to be stored for use at their peak periods, viz. lighting-up time until midnight and perhaps 5.0 a.m. until daylight. Such batteries had formed the commercial footing upon which, by the time the subject of batteries came under the scrutiny of the Garretts, an extensive battery making industry had developed in which the manufacture of traction batteries had a significant part.

The choice of battery types came down to two, the Faure lead/acid and the nickel/iron, the former the older. In a lead/acid battery, plates of lead coated with lead oxide are immersed in an electrolyte of diluted acid whereas in a nickel/iron battery the electrolyte is alkaline and the metal plates are of steel and nickel, though the actual construction is complex. Two leading exemplars of the former type were the Exide-Ironclad, made by the Chloride Electrical Storage Co.Ltd. of Clifton Junction, Manchester, and the Kathanode from the D.P. Battery Company Ltd. of Bakewell, Derbyshire. In the other camp there was the NIFE battery, made under the Swedish Jungner patent by Batteries Ltd. of Redditch, and the Edison, made by Edison Accumulators Ltd. whose office was at 15, Upper George Street, London W1, but whose works were in the United States. Another noted American company was the Philadelphia Storage Battery Company. The initial Garrett choice was the Exide-Ironclad used in No.33119 and many of its successors. Whilst the selection may have been dictated in the first instance by what happened to be available during the War the decision was perspicacious. The makers had a good reputation, particularly in the honouring of their guarantees; had a network of service stations for batteries; and maintained a force of service inspectors to give advice upon the management of the batteries. Exide used a moulded ebonite case. Inside the battery the negative plate consisted of a cast grid of antimonial lead into which the paste was worked. The positive plate was more complicated. Within a lead frame, with overall dimensions the same as the negative plate, were fixed finned lead columns, over the fins of which were fitted horizontally-slit ebonite tubes, provided externally with ribs, into the interior of which, around the lead rods, was packed the lead oxide which formed the active material. Both types of plate had feet which rested on the ebonite ribs in the floor of the case. The plates were assembled in the cases, kept apart by treated wood separators and each group linked together at the top by a lead bridge piece upon which was mounted the terminal post. A moulded ebonite cap with a screwed access plug was placed over the terminals and held down by two lead sealing nuts. For a traction battery the cells were grouped in the battery box, groups of 44 to 60 being common, the posts linked by lead straps with either bolted or burned connections to the posts. Though the principles of the Kathanode batteries were similar, a different, and simpler, approach was made to the problem of retaining the paste on the positive plates by wrapping each plate closely in a jacket of glass fibre felt. Not only did this retain the paste but it also acted as an effective separator and damped down vibrations in the plates caused by rough roads or heedless driving. This method was also followed by the Tudor Accumulator Co. Ltd. whose works were at Dukinfield, in the Manchester conurbation. As already explained, Garretts turned to Tudor in the first instance because of their accommodating approach to the problems of battery shape posed by the GTZ's requirements, a matter in which Chloride had been unable or unwilling to assist.

The nickel/iron battery was completely different in design to the lead/acid type. In the Edison battery the ebonite box was superseded by a nickelled steel box, welded at the seams and with corrugations pressed into the flat faces to give rigidity. The structure and tubes of the positive plates were of nickelled steel. A light frame held together an assembly of perforated tubes (each about ¼" diameter and 4" long) filled in thin layers with nickel hydroxide and metallic nickel flake. The negative plates were made up on the same principle but using oblong pockets filled with iron oxide. The bottom of the box was insulated from the plates by a rubber rack and the separators were also of rubber which was the material used at the ends of the plates to prevent contact with the box. The bridge connectors and terminal posts were steel. The electrolyte used was potassium hydroxide solution. The manufacturers described the reactions involved as follows:

A full account of the very complex internal reactions of an Edison cell is not yet available. An outline of the phenomena involved is, however, quite simple to realize. Considering a new cell we have nickel hydrate in the positive plate, iron oxide in the negative, and both dipping in a strong solution of potassium hydrate. On the first charge the green nickel hydrate becomes more highly oxidised and turns permanently black, whilst the iron oxide is reduced to a chemically pure form of iron. Electrolytic actions also take place in the solution itself, but become immediately neutralised by secondary reactions, which occur between the dissociated potassium hydrate and the large excess of water present. Thus the electrolyte does not enter into chemical union with the active substances of the electrodes, but functions purely as a liquid conductor. On discharging, that is when the unimmersed parts of the plates are joined by a conductor, the iron plate slowly reoxidises, meanwhile that the nickel plate becomes reduced, though never again to the lower and original state of oxidation of green nickel hydrate. The essential fact in the behaviour of the Edison cell when in circuit is the electrolytic carrying of oxygen from the positive plate to the negative during discharging, and a reversal of that process during recharging. For this reason the Edison accumulator has sometimes been called the 'oxygen-lift cell'.

The NIFE battery was first used experimentally by Garretts in 1921 when the U.K. licensees were Batteries Ltd. of Crabbs Cross, Redditch. The actual example used was shipped from the works of Svenska Ackumulator Aktiebolaget Jungner on March 24, 1921. This was tested in a No.3 wagon (No.154) and compared with the same wagon with Chloride batteries and also with the same size of wagon with alternative motors, the tester being Jack Simpson who tabulated his results as follows:

Vehicle	No.3 (standard)	No.3	No.3	No.3
Motor	Vickers	A.G.E.(80 volts)	A.G.E.(60 volts)	A.G.E.(60 volts)
Battery	I.M.V.7	I.M.V.7	N.I.F.E.(280 A/H)	I.M.V.7
Gear Ratio	10.6 to 1	10.6 to 1	15.2 to 1	15.2 to 1
M.P.H. (level)	11	11.75	11.75	14.50
M.P.H. (average)	10.60	11.40	11.40	13.80
Amp/Hrs. per mile	7.30	6.90	7.58	6.50
Miles per charge (test on route)	25 to 27.50	27.50 to 29	34 to 37	27.50 to 30
Current on level	60	62	80	85
Current on 1 in 7.5	340	360	390	390

No sales resulted from this trial. Serve, newly arrived at Leiston, used the results in his efforts to improve both the operating speed and miles per charge of the Garrett electrics. A copy of Jack Simpson's report was sent to Batteries Ltd. on June 9, 1921, and they seem not to have pursued the matter.

The next approach came another way. C.R.D. Pritchett, one of the directors of Pritchett & Gold & E.P.S. Company Ltd, whose works were at Dagenham Dock, Essex, played golf at Aldeburgh where he met Gordon Melrose, newly installed as Managing Director of Richard Garrett & Sons Ltd. Not altogether surprisingly, traction batteries were discussed. Pritchett poured some scorn on Batteries Ltd.'s efforts to sell the NIFE, and mentioned to Melrose that if his own firm had an opportunity to market the NIFE it would make a more energetic job of it. As an upshot Melrose arranged for J.Taylor, Pritchett's technical assistant, to meet W.J. Marshall on April 6, 1922, as a result of which Pritchett & Gold undertook to send a battery to Leiston. After Serve had provided Taylor with dimensional and other information a suitable size of battery was made, and left Dagenham on July 12. The manufacture and despatch was done under a cloak of greatest 'confidentiality', and the battery was supposedly a copy, without licence, of the NIFE. A discharge test on July 19 went off reasonably well, but notwithstanding this, the connection appears to have made little progress and nearly all Garrett vehicles continued to have Exide batteries until the rift over the GTZs occurred. To understand why this was, a study of the price list for the 'C' type provides the answer. The price of the chassis complete (*without* battery or body) was £490. The cost of the batteries available was:

Kathanode	£230	NIFE	£450
Exide Ironclad	£280	Edison type A8	£692

The Kathanode originally carried a two year guarantee, later extended to three; the NIFE and Exide offered three years; and Edison, four.

The only Edison batteries sold were for Nos.265 and 267 ('E' and 'G' types respectively) which had A10 batteries. No.235, for Sheffield Corporation, had a NIFE TK35. No.109, for Boots, poses a mystery. A NIFE catalogue showed it as having a battery by them but it was sold a year before Garretts had any contact with Batteries Ltd. No.311 (Manchester Corporation) had DP Kathanode batteries type KA29 (of 448 A/H capacity). Wagons 266 and 289-295 inclusive, built after the rapport with Tudor was established, had Tudor Ky Dm 17 batteries, whilst all the GTZs had batteries by Tudor. Very nearly everything else had Exide-Ironclad batteries. The smallest of these was an IMV6; the largest, in the 'G' types, an IMV12. The largest battery installation was in No.242 which had a 44 cell IMV12, a total weight of nearly 34 cwt representing nearly 52 cubic feet of battery, requiring a battery tray area of virtually 20 square feet.

Exide-Ironclad CELLS - Type IMV

Type of Cell.	IMV 2	IMV 3	IMV 4	IMV 5	IMV 6	IMV 7	IMV 8	IMV 9	IMV 10	IMV 11	IMV 12
Capacity in Ampere hours :											
When discharging in 5 hours	64	96	129	161	193	226	258	290	323	355	387
„ „ 1 hour	42	63	84	105	126	147	168	189	210	231	252
„ „ ½ hour	33	49	66	82	99	115	132	148	165	181	198
Discharge current in Amperes :											
When discharging in 5 hours	13	19	26	32	39	45	51	58	64	71	77
„ „ 1 hour	42	63	84	105	126	147	168	189	210	231	252
„ „ ½ hour	66	99	132	165	198	231	264	297	330	363	396
Charge current in Amperes :											
Starting : for regular charge	11	16	22	27	32	38	43	48	54	59	65
Finishing :	4½	6½	9	11	13	16	18	20	22	24	26
Equalising for periodical overcharge	2½	3½	4½	5½	6½	8	9	10	11	12	13
Outside dimensions of Cells only — Length (Inches)	2 15/16	2 15/16	3 11/16	4 7/16	5 3/16	5 15/16	6 11/16	7 7/16	8 3/16	8 15/16	9 11/16
Length (M/ms.)	56	75	94	113	132	151	170	189	208	227	246
Width (Inches)	6 5/16	6 5/16	6 5/16	6 5/16	6 5/16	6 5/16	6 5/16	6 5/16	6 5/16	6 5/16	6 5/16
Width (M/ms.)	160	160	160	160	160	160	160	160	160	160	160
Height (Inches)	13 5/8	13 5/8	13 5/8	13 5/8	13 5/8	13 5/8	13 5/8	13 5/8	13 5/8	13 5/8	13 5/8
Overall (M/ms.)	346	346	346	346	346	346	346	346	346	346	346
Weight of Cell complete with acid (lbs.)	18	24	30	36	42	48	54	60	66	73	79
(kgs.)	8.2	10.9	13.6	16.3	19	21.7	24.5	27.2	30	33.1	35.8
Weight per Cell in standard tray, complete with fittings, etc. approx. (lbs.)	21	27	34	40	46	53	59	65	71	79	85
(kgs.)	9.5	12.2	15.4	18.1	21	24	26.7	29.5	32.2	35.8	38.5

Perhaps the best commentary on why this sales pattern should have been so is contained in the report prepared by Mr. C.W. Marshall for the I.M.E.A. Convention held in Glasgow in 1926, the information being based upon the experience obtained with the varied electric vehicle fleet operated by the Corporation of Glasgow over the preceding thirteen years. At the time he spoke the lead acid battery, being cheaper in first cost and as effective in service, was favoured by the Corporation. He noted that alkaline batteries then cost from two to four times the price of lead batteries, although they had a life of at least five to six years in hard service, compared with perhaps three or four years for a lead/acid type. Their good life characteristics were negated, in some degree, by their high internal resistance and low watt-hour efficiency. Marshall's figures for the two types of battery used by Garretts were as follows:

Type of Battery	Alkaline	Lead (thick plate)
Watt-hour efficiency in per cent	59	75
Watt-hours per cubic inch	0.74	0.6
Watt-hours per pound	15	9
Approx. initial cost in £ per kw.h	30	8
Life in years	6-8	3
Life in cycles of charge and discharge	1800-2400	900

Table of batteries available in Garrett vehicles, based upon list issued to salesmen, current 1924.

*The No.3 wagon was also offered with an Edison A8 (but none were sold).

The list quoted 88 volt motors with lead/acid batteries and 60 volt with the alkaline type.

Vehicle	Chloride		D.P.		NIFE K-72v	Edison
	Std. size	Max. size	Std. size	Max. size	One size	One size
No.3 (1½t)	IMV 6	IMV 8	TR 19	TR 25	TK 24	A 6 *
	193 AH	259 AH	215 AH	288 AH	240 AH	225 AH
No.4 (2½t)	IMV 7	IMV9[11tray	TR 21	TR 31	TK 30	A 8
	226 AH	290 AH	240 AH	360 AH	300 AH	300 AH
No.4 (tipper)	IMV 8	IMV 9	TR 23	TR 31	TK 30	A 8
	259 AH	290 AH	260 AH	360 AH	300 AH	300 AH
No.5 (3½t)	IMV 9	IMV 10	TR 27	TR 35	TK 38	A 10
	290 AH	323 AH	310 AH	418 AH	380 AH	375 AH
No.5 (tipper)	IMV 9	IMV 10	TR 27	TR 35	TK 38	A 10
	290 AH	323 AH	310 AH	418 AH	380 AH	375 AH
No.5(sidetip	IMV 10	IMV 10	TR 27	TR 35	TK 38	A 12
	323 AH	323 AH	310 AH	418 AH	380 AH	450 AH
'G'		IMV 12	TR 33	TR 35	TK 45	A 12
		385 AH		418 AH	455 AH	450 AH
'C'	IMV9[12tray	IMV9[12tray	TR 27	TR 27	TK 30	A 10
			310 AH	310 AH	300 AH	375 AH

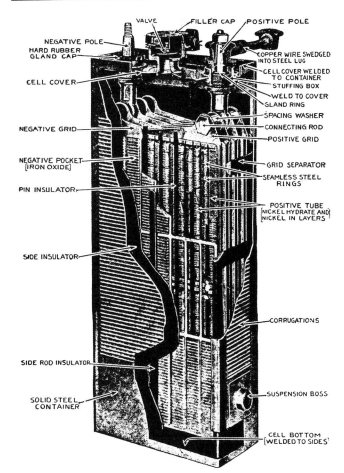

Fig.147. Cut-away drawing of the Edison cell showing the method of connecting the positive and negative plates to each other and to their respective terminal posts.

Fig.148. *This rear end view of a completed chassis shows how large a space the battery box, in this case with part of its complement of Exide-Ironclad cells, occupied. The picture shows, too, the position and hanging of the Vickers motor (with the cover removed from the brushes), the case around the silent chain drive forward to the counter shaft and the double roller chains back to the drive sprockets. It also shows clearly the layout of the hand and foot brakes, and the foot operated controller (with its cover removed).*

Tender and Specification for 6-wheeled Trolley Buses for Bradford Corporation Tramways
(not accepted)

TENDER for the supply of
DOUBLE-DECK SIX-WHEEL ELECTRIC TROLLEY VEHICLES
_____

To the TRAMWAYS COMMITTEE of the BRADFORD CORPORATION

Gentlemen,
We, the undersigned, hereby offer to supply and deliver to your Committee at the Stores at the Thornbury Car Depot
     6 DOUBLE-DECK SIX-WHEEL ELECTRIC TROLLEY VEHICLES, COMPLETE   @   £2225-0-0 each
according to Specification and I.E.E. Conditions of Contract revised January, 1926, for the sum of two thousand two
hundred and twenty five pounds each, and to deliver the same at the said Stores within approximately 18/20 weeks from
date of written order. See letter dated 15/3/30.
And we hereby undertake and agree to carry out the Contracts Clauses of the Corporation, and that until a formal Contract
is entered into this Tender when accepted by the Committee shall constitute a binding Contract.

                                   Signed   For RICHARD GARRETT & SONS LTD.
                                   Address: Leiston Works, Suffolk
Date: March 15th 1930.
Subject to conditions of sale as per sheet No.530 insofar as they apply.

SPECIFICATION
of
GARRETT 'OS' TYPE SIX WHEELED ELECTRIC TROLLEY BUS CHASSIS
_____

GENERAL. The Chassis is of the six-wheeled type, i.e. two front steering wheels and four rear driving wheels, each rear
     wheel being fitted with a suitable brake. The frame, springs, axles, steering gear, brakes and wheels are of
     ample size and capable of carrying a load of passengers equal to 50% above the seating capacity of the Body,
     to comply with the conditions under the heading of 'Performance' in your specification dated 3/3/30.
     The design of the chassis permits of all wearing parts being easily replaced, and special care has been given to
     accessibility. The springing of the vehicle is such as to reduce to a minimum shocks and vibrations due to bad
     road surfaces, and to prevent undue side rolling of the bus, especially when carrying a light load.
     All working joints are water and dust-proof.
FRAME. This is of 35 ton pressed steel, with side members of deep section and good proportions, suitably stiffened with
     cross members securely fixed in position.
BRACKETS. All brackets are of the best quality cast steel, secured to the frame with perfect fitting 3% nickel steel bolts
     and nuts.
SPRINGS. Special attention has been given to the design of the springs, which are of Silico-Manganese steel. All wearing
     eyes are fitted with gunmetal bushes, pressed into place. Front and rear springs are underslung on nickel
     chrome steel bolts.
FRONT AXLE. This is of the centre-point steering type. The front axle bed is a 40 ton tensile steel stamping of substantial
     I section. The steering pivots work in well-lubricated bronze bushes, the weight being taken by a ball thrust
     washer.
STEERING GEAR. The steering gear has been designed to meet the requirements of a six-wheeled vehicle. A hardened
     worm and worm-wheel are fitted, mounted on ball bearings throughout. The actual gear, being high up in the
     driver's cab, is very accessible and well protected from dust and dirt thrown up by the front wheels. This gear,
     in conjunction with the centre-point steering feature of the front axle, requires the minimum of effort in operation
     and renders the control of the vehicle extremely easy in traffic. The steering wheel is of ample size and
     approved design.
REAR AXLES. The complete rear axle assembly is by the Kirkstall Forge Co., embodying the well-known features of their
     design, which includes the third Differential.
ROAD WHEELS. High tensile disc wheels are used. Single 40" x 8" Dunlop pneumatic tyres are fitted on all wheels, and
     are interchangeable all round.
BRAKES. A set of Brakes is fitted to each of the four rear and two front wheels. The four rear and two front wheel brakes
     are each operated by an air cylinder acting direct on the camshaft lever and controlled by a pedal in the driver's
     cab. A hand brake is provided to operate on the rear wheels. The Brake surfaces are of generous dimensions
     and each set of brakes is capable of stopping and holding the vehicle when fully loaded on a gradient of 1 in 8.
     The brake drums are removable independently of the hub, and are provided with renewable cast iron liners. The
     brake shoes are lined with die-pressed Ferodo Fabric. Special attention has been given to the position and
     design of the adjusting screws on the brake rods to facilitate quick and easy adjustment when the vehicle is in
     service. The pneumatic brake equipment consists of a motor-driven and automatically controlled compressor,
     six operating cylinders and one foot valve, the latter being worked by a pedal.
TRANSMISSION GEAR. The power is transmitted direct to the foremost of the two rear axles through a tubular propeller
     shaft fitted at both ends with suitable universal joints; the front joint is a flexible coupling of the 'Hardy' disc type,
     centred with a spherical bearing to relieve the disc of the weight of the shaft, thus eliminating the possible
     vibration. The rear joint is a universal joint. The flexible connections between the two rear axles are in
     accordance with Kirkstall's standard design.

MOTOR. A standard 80 HP R.V. Motor by Bull Motors Ltd. is fitted, to comply fully with the particulars given in your specification under the heading of 'Motors', and otherwise in accordance with the following specification and performance curves RVC.69 attached.

MOTORS

Frame.   Box type steel casting, octagonal in shape with mild steel brackets.

Bearings.   Roller bearings at each end, double thrust ball bearings at commutator end. The bearings are arranged in separate housings in such a way that the armature can be withdrawn from the machine with its bearings in place in their housings, and remaining undisturbed in position on the shaft. The commutator can be re-turned without removing the bearings from the shaft or altering their adjustment.

Shafts.   These are of exceptionally large diameter, turned from high tensile nickel steel bar. All parts are well radiused and rapid change of section is avoided.

Main Poles.   These are built up with laminations and are riveted under heavy hydraulic pressure and secured to the yoke by means of large hexagonal headed screws.

Interpoles.   These are machined from steel bar and fixed to the yoke by means of countersunk hexagonal headed screws.

Fans.   These are light alloy castings mounted on a spigot at the rear end of the armature and accurately balanced.

Commutators.   These are built up of hard drawn copper sections, insulated with pure mica, and mounted on cast steel bushes and vee rings, providing a long leakage surface. The commutator rises are exceptionally wide and are integral with the commutator section.

Armature Cores.   These are built up of thin Lohy's steel laminations insulated with special varnish. Thick supporting plates are fitted to both core ends. The cores are mounted on a light cast steel hub removable from the shaft. Light alloy winding carriers are mounted at both ends of the core and the rear carrier forms a complete protecting shield for the projecting portions of the windings.

Armature Windings.   Asbestos and double cotton-covered, hard-drawn, high conductivity copper strip is used for the Armature coils. The coils, after being wound, are impregnated and insulated with thick mica troughs taped on. The armature is banded with 16 s.w.g. high tensile steel wire, to provide for overspeeds up to 3000 r.p.m. The winding carriers are covered on the outside with substantial canvas and covers.

Field and Interpole Windings.   These are wound with rectangular section asbestos and double cotton strip, completely enclosed with mica wrappings and strong web tape. The coils are held firmly in place by stiff spring steel washers placed between the coils and the yoke. Heavy cast aluminium washers are fitted at the opposite ends of the coils to ensure ample distribution of pressure over their whole surface.

Brush Gear.   The brush boxes are of the totally enclosed type, arranged to exclude all dust and dirt from the sliding surfaces of the brush slot. The brush springs and finger lie within the brush box enclosure and are, therefore, protected from dust and dirt. Brush boxes are designed to occupy a very small arc, and provide exceptionally wide clearance between brush arms.

Terminal Leads.   Flexible V.I.R. Cable, braided all over with cord is used for the terminal leads, which are brought out through lead bushed holes in the end brackets.

Ventilation.   Air enters through aluminium cowls formed in the inspection cover openings or fitted to the commutator end bracket, and passes by parallel paths through the commutator and armature core vents and between the main field and interpole coils, being exhausted to the atmosphere through vents opening in an axial direction in the rear end bracket.

Vacuum Impregnation.   All windings are impregnated before assembly, and the finished armature, field and interpole coils are again fully impregnated on completion.

Accessibility.   Large removable doors are fitted at the top and bottom over the commutator. These doors extend practically the whole width of the Motor and provide an exceptional degree of accessibility.

CONTROLLER. The vehicle is equipped with a foot-operated contactor type controller of B.T.H. Co.'s manufacture, of ample capacity, insulated from the chassis by porcelain insulators.

RESISTANCES. The resistances are of the E.M.B. unbreakable type, of large capacity, insulated from the chassis by porcelain insulators.

CIRCUIT BREAKERS. These are of the Dick Kerr 400 amp. type, with magnetic blow-out, and are capable of being operated by hand if necessary.

TRACTION WIRING. The necessary wiring for connecting the motor, controller and resistances etc. from the trolley bases is of cab tyre sheathed cable of 248/.018, 163/.018, 2500 megohm grade.

TROLLEY BASES. The 'Bradford' type trolley bases are of Brecknell, Willis & Co.'s manufacture. The trolley arms are of the best tapered steel tubes, made by Messrs. Stewarts & Lloyds.

SKATE EQUIPMENT. This is of the flexible cable trailing type, with cast iron shoe to run in the groove of a tram rail.

TURNING CIRCLE. The vehicle is capable of being turned completely between two kerbs 54 ft. apart.

GROUND CLEARANCE. This complies with the requirements of the Ministry of Transport Regulations.

TOOLS, etc. A full kit of tools is supplied as under:-

      'Skyhi' Lifting Jack.
      Set of tools and accessories for pneumatic tyres.
      Spanners ¼" to 1".
      Adjustable Spanner.
      Screwdrivers 9" and 3".
      Hand Hammer.
      Chisel-ended Bar.
      Special Spanners for rear wheel lock nut.
      Oil Can (one pint).
      Tecalemit Grease Gun with Booster Gun and flexible pipe.

BODY. Manufactured by Messrs. Charles Roe & Sons, Crossgates, Leeds, and generally in accordance with your Specification, and complying with Ministry of Transport requirements.

THE MOTORS. All of the Motors fitted to Garrett Electric Trolley Buses are manufactured for us by our Associated Company, Messrs. Bull Motors, of Ipswich, consequently when considering the claims which we make for the Garrett chassis Tramway Managers can be assured that **the interests of the manufacturers of the chassis and motor,** which is so important a feature of the chassis, **are identical.**

For the Four-Wheel chassis, we are in a position to supply either a single 50 Nominal H. P. 500-550 volt series wound Motor, or two twin 35 Nominal H.P. each 500-550 volt series wound motors, with or without electrical braking attachment.

For the Six-Wheel chassis, we are in a position to supply either a single 60 Nominal H.P. 500 volt series wound motor, or two twin 40 Nominal H.P. each 500 to 550 volt series wound motors, with or without electrical braking attachment.

As to whether it is advisable to use a single or double motor equipment, this will depend very largely on the nature of the route to be traversed, the gradients to be negotiated and the exigencies of the proposed service.

As the Motor may be described as the heart of the Trolley Bus, we are giving an abbreviated specification describing the main features, as there are many points of interest in the design and construction of the Bull Motor. Where the construction of the twin motors differs from the single motor, the details are given separately in each case.

GENERAL METHOD OF CONSTRUCTION. Single Motors are of the ventilated type of 50 or 60 Nominal H.P. at 1060 R.P.M. at one hour rating and are in accordance with B.E.S.A. Specification No. 173 of 1923.

Twin Motors are of the twin armature type, having two completely independent armatures built up, with their commutators, on cast steel spiders, and both mounted back to back on the same shaft which is extended at one end and is arranged to transmit the full torque of both armatures. The armatures are mounted in octagonal steel box type frames, bolted together on the vertical centre line between the two machines.

FRAME. Box type steel casting, octagonal in shape, with cast steel end brackets.

END BRACKETS. Two cast steel—or alternatively aluminium alloy—end brackets are provided with large inspection openings giving ready access to the commutators and brush gear.

END BRACKETS (for twin motors). The end brackets at the drive and non drive ends of the machine consist of heavily ribbed high tensile aluminium castings provided with suitable facings inside to carry the brush rocker. Steel housings are fitted in these brackets to carry the bearing assemblies.

BEARINGS. Roller bearing at each end, double thrust ball bearings at commutator end. The bearings are arranged in separate housings in such a way that the armature can be withdrawn from the machine with its bearing in place in their housings, and remaining undisturbed in position on the shaft. The commutator can be re-turned without removing the bearings from the shaft or altering their adjustment.

BEARINGS (for twin motors). Three roller bearings are provided, one at the drive end, one in the centre between the two armatures and one at the non drive end.

A double thrust ball race is also fitted at the non drive end. The centre bearing is supported in a steel housing mounted in a circular aluminium dividing wall which is spigotted and bolted between the circular facings on the ends of the two magnet frames.

VS 819

Standard 50 H.P. Bull Series Wound Motor.

SHAFTS. These are of exceptionally large diameter, turned from high tensile nickel steel bar. All parts are well radiused and rapid change of section is avoided.

MAIN POLES. These are built up with laminations and are rivetted under heavy hydraulic pressure and secured to the yoke by means of large hexagonal headed screws.

INTERPOLES. These are machined from steel bar and fixed to the yoke by means of countersunk hexagonal headed screws.

FANS. Fans are built up from steel plate and are mounted on a facing and spigot on the rear end of the winding carrier.

COMMUTATORS. These are built up of hard drawn copper sections, insulated with pure mica and mounted on cast steel bushes and vee rings, providing a long leakage surface. The commutator risers are exceptionally wide and are integral with the commutator sections.

ESTABLISHED OVER 150 YEARS

ARMATURE CORES. These are built of thin Lohys Steel laminations insulated with special varnish. Thick supporting plates are fitted to both core ends. Cast steel winding carriers are fitted thus forming a solid centre to which the end windings are securely bedded down. In the case of twin motors the winding carriers are of alluminium alloy.

ARMATURE SPIDERS (for twin motors). The armature spiders which carry both armatures and commutators are bored taper, and held on to their shafts by means of a large fine thread nut. Both armatures can easily be removed from their shafts by removing the commutator end brackets.

The Armature Core.

The Magnet Ring, showing the armature windings.

ARMATURE WINDINGS. Asbestos and double cotton covered hard drawn high conductivity copper strip is used for the Armature coils. The coils after being wound are impregnated and insulated with thick mica troughs taped on. The Armature is banded with 16 S.W.G. high tensile steel wire. **The motor being safe up to overspeeds of 3000 r.p.m.** The winding carriers are insulated with mica and the windings are covered on the outside with substantial canvas end covers.

FIELD AND INTERPOLE WINDINGS. These are wound with rectangular section asbestos and double cotton covered strip, completely enclosed, with mica wrappings and strong web tape. The coils are held firmly in place by stiff spring steel washers placed between the coils and the yoke. Heavy cast aluminium washers are fitted at the opposite ends of the coils to ensure ample distribution of pressure over their whole surface.

BRUSH GEAR. Square section brass brush arms are fitted and are covered with moulded insulation, giving ample leakage surface. These are fitted with cast brass brush boxes with cast brass pressure fingers actuated by robust spiral springs made from steel strip.

The body of the box forms a shield which protects the spring from damage due to accidental arcing or short circuits.

TERMINAL LEADS. Flexible V.I.R. cable, braided over all with cord is used for the terminal leads which are brought out through lead bushed holes in the end brackets.

VENTILATION. Air enters through aluminium cowls formed in the inspection cover openings or fitted to the commutator end bracket, and passes by parallel paths through the commutator and armature core vents and between the main field and interpole coils, being exhausted to the atmosphere through vents opening in an axial direction in the rear end bracket.

VENTILATION (for twin motors). A row of ventilating openings for the ventilating fan discharge is provided for each motor, one row on each side of the centre flanged joint.

Bull 50 H.P. Series wound Motor fitted with air vent, principally for use in very dusty climates.

Garrett Electric Vehicles

Works No	Reg No	Date	Type	Owner	Notes
33119	BJ3396	14/05/17	No. 5	Great Eastern Railway, Ipswich,Suffolk.	
102	BJ4488	01/08/19	No. 5et	Blackpool Corporation, Lancs.	With 10cwt crane.
103	BJ4874	06/02/20	No. 4	Lancs. & Yorks. Rly., Manchester.	No. 50
104	BJ4801	02/01/20	No. 4	Lancs. & Yorks. Rly., Manchester.	No. 51
105	BJ4516	20/09/19	No. 4	Siddall & Hilton, Sowerby Bridge, WR Yorks.	The Standard Wire Co.
106	BJ4605	23/10/19	No. 5	Morgans Brewery Co., Norwich	
107	BJ4795	19/12/19	No. 3	GN, GC & GE Rlys.	
		28/06/20		AGE Demonstration.	
		23/03/21		Metropolitan Borough of Stepney.	
108	BJ4796	19/12/19	No. 3	GN, GC & GE Rlys.	
		08/06/20		Boots Pure Drug Co.Ltd., Nottingham.	
109	BJ4873	10/01/20	No. 3	Boots Pure Drug Co.Ltd., Nottingham.	Originally ordered by GN,GC & GE Rlys.
110	BJ5025	24/04/20	No. 3	Redgates Ltd., Nottingham.	Originally ordered by GN,GC & GE Rlys.
111	BJ5155	29/05/20	No. 3	Jewson & Sons, Norwich.	Originally ordered by GN,GC & GE Rlys.
112	BJ4885	24/03/20	No. 4	Eastern Counties Farmers Coop., Ipswich.	
113	BJ4614	25/02/20	No. 4et	Glasgow Corporation	Modified 11/21
114	BJ5015	30/03/20	No. 4	Holdsworth Bros., Plumstead, Kent.	
115	BJ4886	24/03/20	No. 4	Weston & Westall.	
116	BJ4882	30/06/20	No. 4	E.H.Vyse, North Shields, Northumberland.	
		04/25		E.C.Robson & Sons, Sunderland.	
117	BJ4887	24/03/20	No. 4	Weston & Westall.	
118	BJ5161	07/06/20	No. 4et	Sheffield Corporation.	
119			No.4	Not made.	
120	EH1816	31/03/20	No. 5	North Staffordshire Railway, Stoke on Trent.	No. 20 Removeable body.
121	CH2011	17/05/20	No. 5	Midland Railway, Derby.	
122	Export	14/04/20	No. 3	Butlers (London) Ltd.	Returned to RG&S 4/22 and broken up.
123		/20	No. 5	Dublin Demonstration.	Broken up.
124	BJ5587	25/09/20	No. 4et	Colne Corporation, Lancs.	Royal Show.
125	BJ5150	13/03/20	No. 5	Talbot-Stead Tube Co., Walsall, Staffs.	
126	BJ5160	07/06/20	No. 3	Boots Pure Drug Co., Nottingham.	
127	BJ5608	26/11/20	No. 3	Savoy Hotel Ltd., London.	
128	BJ5594	04/11/20	No. 3	Savoy Hotel Ltd., London.	
129	BJ5609	11/12/20	No. 3	Savoy Hotel Ltd., London.	
130			No. 5et	Royal Show	No platform, body or cab.
	BJ5606	23/11/20		Borough of South Shields., Co. Durham.	
131	BJ5607	24/11/20	No. 4et	Borough of Harwich.	
132			No. 4	AGE London Showroom.	Dummy motor, battery & tyres. Became No. 219.
133	BJ5516	04/09/20	No. 4	E.C.Robson & Sons, Sunderland.	Per Christy Bros,Chelmsford.
134	BJ5524	18/09/20	No. 4	E.C.Robson & Sons, Sunderland.	Per Christy Bros,Chelmsford.
135	BJ5527	21/09/20	No. 4	C.Vaux & Sons, Sunderland.	Per Newcastle Electric Supply Co.
136			2½	Demonstrator at Dundee.	Scottish Motor Exhibition.
		09/06/22		Glasgow Corporation.	No. 105
137		24/12/21	2½	L&SWR Southampton Docks.	Originally for Campania Nacional, Barcelona.
138			2½vet	RG&S Works Use.	Stockton on Tees Demonstration.
139		25/08/21	2½	Spillers & Bakers, Bristol.	
140	XC9889	21/10/21	2½et	Derby Corporation.	No. 7 ex A.G.E. demonstration.
141	WA4761	20/08/21	2½et	Sheffield Corporation.	No. 32
142	WA4762	09/07/21	2½et	Sheffield Corporation.	No. 33
143	WA4763	01/07/21	2½et	Sheffield Corporation.	No. 34
144	BJ5604	16/11/20	No. 5	Mann, Crossman & Paulin Ltd.	
145	Export	01/06/21	3½et	Calcutta Corporation, India.	Per J.Birch & Co. With 10cwt crane
146	BJ5614	09/20	No. 5	Demonstrator	Commercial Motor and Brewers Exhibitions.
	BJ5973	23/12/20		L&NWR (Demonstration)	Returned to RG&S and broken up.
147	Export	01/06/21	3½et	Calcutta Corporation, India.	Per J.Birch & Co. With 10cwt crane
148	WA4929	09/21	2½	AGE Sheffield Demonstration.	
		03/10/22		Jewson & Sons, Norwich.	
149	WA4764	29/07/21	2½et	Sheffield Corporation.	No. 35
150	WA4765	09/07/21	2½et	Sheffield Corporation.	No. 36
151	BJ5611	04/12/20	No. 5vet	Fife Electric Power Co.	Per Balfour Beatty & Co.Ltd.
152	Export	09/02/21	1½	Griffin Eng. Co.Ltd., Johannesburg, S.A.	
153	Export	06/07/21	1½	J.H.Dryden, Buenos Aires.	For demonstration in South America.
154		20/03/22	1½	W&R Jacob, Liverpool.	
		20/07/33		Wolsey Ltd., Leicester.	
155	WA4766	16/07/21	2½et	Sheffield Corporation.	No. 37
156	WA4767	23/07/21	2½et	Sheffield Corporation.	No. 38
157	WA4768	27/07/21	2½et	Sheffield Corporation.	No. 39
158	WA4769	29/07/21	2½et	Sheffield Corporation.	No. 40
159	WA4770	29/07/21	2½et	Sheffield Corporation.	No. 41
160	NO3630	29/09/21	3½et	Colchester Corporation Demonstration.	
		23/08/22		Bedford Corporation	
161	FN5207	02/09/21	2½vet	Canterbury City Council, Kent	No. 2
		01/08/30		Hackney Borough Council.	
162		13/09/21	3½et	Hampstead Borough Council.	No. 5
163		01/07/21	No. 3	Nuttall & Co.Ltd., Blackburn, Lancs.	Windscreen fitted.
164	OH3859	23/09/21	3½et	City of Birmingham.	No. 33 Chain drive.

Works No	Reg No	Date	Type	Owner	Notes
165	OH3860	27/09/21	3½et	City of Birmingham.	No. 34 Chain drive.
166		05/10/21	2½et	Norwich Corporation.	No. 31
167		05/10/21	2½et	Norwich Corporation.	No. 32
168		14/10/21	2½et	East Ham Borough Council.	Steel body.
169		21/10/21	2½et	East Ham Borough Council.	Steel body.
170		13/10/21	2½et	East Ham Borough Council.	Steel body.
171		24/12/21	2½	L&SWR Southampton Docks.	Commercial Motor Exhibition.
172		08/10/21	3½	London Demonstrator.	Brewers Exhibition; rebuilt as 2½t No.209.
173		11/21	2½et	Demonstrator.	Roads & Transport Exhibition.
	XW9068	02/05/22		Hampstead Borough Council.	No. 6
174		/21	3½	Cardiff & St.Albans Demonstrator.	Demonstrated to Wm.Burgess (Bristol) Ltd.
		24/04/26		Norwich Corporation.	No. 36 Secondhand
175			1½	Not made.	
176		/21	No. 3	Stock	Chassis only for sale by Receiver /32
177		06/01/22	2½et	L&SWR Southampton Docks.	
178		06/01/22	2½et	L&SWR Southampton Docks.	
179		17/07/22	No. 3	City of Birmingham.	No. 38 Chain drive.
180		17/07/22	No. 3	City of Birmingham.	No. 39 Chain drive.
181		26/07/22	No. 3	City of Birmingham.	No. 40 Chain drive.
182		22/11/22	3½et	St.Pancras Borough Council.	No. 3
183		01/12/22	3½et	St.Pancras Borough Council.	No. 4
184	Export	05/12/22	2½	Rangoon Electric Tramways & Supply Co.	Per J.Birch & Co
185	XM6395	08/01/23	4/5vet	Hackney Borough Council.	Electricity Dept.
186		26/04/23	2½et	Norwich Corporation.	No 33, Special kerbside control.
187		26/04/23	2½et	Norwich Corporation.	No 34, Special kerbside control.
188		22/12/22	C	J&B.Stevenson, Glasgow.	Chassis to R.Mitchell & Sons Ltd., Glasgow
189	XR5571	16/05/23	4/5.	Hackney Borough Council.	Surveyors Dept., No. 5
190	XR5572	16/05/23	4/5.	Hackney Borough Council.	Surveyors Dept., No. 6
191	XR5573	16/05/23	4/5.	Hackney Borough Council.	Surveyors Dept., No. 7
192	XR5574	26/05/23	4/5.	Hackney Borough Council.	Surveyors Dept., No. 8
193	XR5575	26/05/23	4/5.	Hackney Borough Council.	Surveyors Dept., No. 9
194	XR5576	26/05/23	4/5.	Hackney Borough Council.	Surveyors Dept., No. 10
195	XR5577	26/05/23	4/5.	Hackney Borough Council.	Surveyors Dept., No. 11
196	XR5578	23/06/23	4/5.	Hackney Borough Council.	Surveyors Dept., No. 12
197	XR5579	23/06/23	4/5.	Hackney Borough Council.	Surveyors Dept., No. 13
198	XR5580	23/06/23	4/5.	Hackney Borough Council.	Surveyors Dept., No. 14
199	XR5581	23/06/23	4/5.	Hackney Borough Council.	Surveyors Dept., No. 15
200	XR5582	02/07/23	4/5.	Hackney Borough Council.	Surveyors Dept., No. 16
201	XR5583	02/07/23	4/5.	Hackney Borough Council.	Surveyors Dept., No. 17
202	XR5584	02/07/23	4/5.	Hackney Borough Council.	Surveyors Dept., No. 18
203	XR5585	02/07/23	4/5.	Hackney Borough Council.	Surveyors Dept., No. 19
204	XR5586	11/07/23	4/5.	Hackney Borough Council.	Surveyors Dept., No. 20
205	XR5587	11/07/23	4/5.	Hackney Borough Council.	Surveyors Dept., No. 21
206	XR5588	03/08/23	4/5.	Hackney Borough Council.	Surveyors Dept., No. 22
207	XR5589	03/08/23	4/5.	Hackney Borough Council.	Surveyors Dept., No. 23
208	XR5590	03/08/23	4/5.	Hackney Borough Council.	Surveyors Dept., No. 24
209		16/06/23	2½et	Hampstead Borough Council.	No. 7; originally No. 172.
210		16/06/23	2½et	Hampstead Borough Council.	No. 8
211		16/06/23	2½et	Hampstead Borough Council.	No. 9
212	RT279		C	Demonstrator.	Broken up by 5/4/28
213	NK6224	24/09/23	3½et	City of St. Albans.	Kerbside control.
214		24/11/23	2½et	Rugby UDC, Warks.	Kerbside control
215			2½et	Not made	Ordered by Rugby UDC but cancelled.
216		25/10/24	2½et	City of Leicester	
217		04/12/23	2½et	City of Leicester	
218		25/10/24	2½et	City of Leicester	
219	TA6777	08/10/23	2½et	Ilfracombe UDC	Originally No.132. Returned to Garretts by 12/25.
		12/25		RG&S	For sale by Receiver /32
220		31/07/24	C2	Borough of Grimsby.	Originally for Andrews & Beaven Ltd., NZ.
221			C	Demonstrated to J.Lyons & Co.Ltd.	Not sold, rebuilt as C2
	Export	28/09/25	C2	Clark & Fauset, Brisbane, Queensland.	Chassis only.
222	HJ3190	30/10/23	3½et	Borough of Southend.	Kerbside control.
223	HJ3191	30/10/23	3½et	Borough of Southend.	Kerbside control.
224	HJ3192	30/10/23	3½et	Borough of Southend.	Kerbside control.
225	HJ3193	30/10/23	3½et	Borough of Southend.	Kerbside control.
226	PD7697	06/11/23	2½et	Barnes UDC, Surrey.	
227	WA9280	22/12/23	5ton	Sheffield Corporation.	No. 55 Chain driven.
228	WA9281	18/01/24	5ton	Sheffield Corporation.	No. 56 Chain driven.
229	WA9282	15/12/23	5ton	Sheffield Corporation.	No. 57 Chain driven.
230	WA9283	19/12/23	5ton	Sheffield Corporation.	No. 58 Chain driven.
231	WA9284	04/01/24	5ton	Sheffield Corporation.	No. 59 Chain driven.
232	WA9285	31/12/23	5ton	Sheffield Corporation.	No. 60 Chain driven.
233	WA9286	11/01/24	5ton	Sheffield Corporation.	No. 61 Chain driven.
234	WA9287	30/01/24	5ton	Sheffield Corporation.	No. 62 Chain driven.
235	WA9288	31/01/24	5ton	Sheffield Corporation.	No. 63 Chain driven.
236	WA9289	12/02/24	GT	Sheffield Corporation.	No. 64 Worm driven.
237	OL1463	25/02/24	GT	City of Birmingham.	No. 41

Garrett Electric Vehicles

Works No	Reg No	Date	Type	Owner	Notes
238	OL1464	21/03/24	GT	City of Birmingham.	No. 42
239	OL1465	26/03/24	GT	City of Birmingham.	No. 43
240	OL1466	29/03/24	GT	City of Birmingham.	No. 44
241	OL1467	31/03/24	GT	City of Birmingham.	No. 45
242		16/07/24	GTS	Norwich Corporation.	No. 35 Six-wheeler.
243		14/10/24	2½et	Felixstowe UDC.	
244		31/01/25	4/5.	Hackney Borough Council.	No. 25
245		31/01/25	4/5.	Hackney Borough Council.	No. 26
246		31/01/25	4/5.	Hackney Borough Council.	No. 27
247		26/01/25	3½et	Borough of Southend.	
248	OM4314	27/05/25	GT	City of Birmingham.	No. 57
249	OM4315	06/06/25	GT	City of Birmingham.	No. 58
250	OM4316	30/05/25	GT	City of Birmingham.	No. 59
251	OM4317	10/06/25	GT	City of Birmingham.	No. 60
252	OM4318	12/06/25	GT	City of Birmingham.	No. 61
253	OM4319	17/06/25	GT	City of Birmingham.	No. 62
254	OM4320	25/06/25	GT	City of Birmingham.	No. 63
255	OM4321	11/07/25	GT	City of Birmingham.	No. 64
256	OM4322	16/07/25	GT	City of Birmingham.	No. 65
257	OM4323	16/07/25	GT	City of Birmingham.	No. 66
258	OM4324	18/07/25	GT	City of Birmingham.	No. 67
259	OM4325	27/07/25	GT	City of Birmingham.	No. 68
260				Number not used.	
261	UM1755	7/25	S	Demonstrator	Roe 37 seat body.
		05/02/27		City of Bradford.	No. 536
262	RT1345	29/10/25	O	Demonstrator	Strachan & Brown 37 seat body. C.M. Show.
		30/11/26		City of Bradford.	No. 535 (as 35 seater).
263		29/10/25	C2	Demonstrator.	Commercial Motor Show. Kerbside control.
	Export	06/01/28		Automobile Electric Supply Co. (Cape) Ltd., SA.	
264	DX5533	24/02/26	ET	Borough of Ipswich	No. 7 Worm driven
265		04/03/26	ET	City of Nottingham.	Worm driven
266	TO2227	03/03/26	G	Boots Pure Drug Co., Nottingham.	
267		14/01/27	G	Hovis Ltd., Battersea, London.	
268		/26	ET	Built for Gillingham Demonstration.	
	Export	02/03/28	E	Automobile Electric Supply Co. (Cape) Ltd., SA.	
269	ON2851	09/04/26	GT	City of Birmingham.	
270	ON2852	30/04/26	GT	City of Birmingham.	
271	ON2853	07/06/26	GT	City of Birmingham.	
272	ON2854	16/06/26	GT	City of Birmingham.	
273	DX5626*	03/03/26	O	Ipswich Corporation	No. 21. Strachan & Brown 30 seat body.
274	DX5623*	03/04/26	O	Ipswich Corporation.	No. 22. Strachan & Brown 30 seat body.
275	DX5624*	04/05/26	O	Ipswich Corporation.	No. 23. Strachan & Brown 30 seat body.
276	DX5625*	30/04/26	O	Ipswich Corporation.	No. 24. Strachan & Brown 30 seat body.
277	DX5628*	02/06/26	O	Ipswich Corporation.	No. 25. Strachan & Brown 30 seat body.
278	DX5629*	17/05/26	O	Ipswich Corporation.	No. 26. Strachan & Brown 30 seat body.
279	DX5627*	28/05/26	O	Ipswich Corporation.	No. 27. Strachan & Brown 30 seat body.
280	DX5630*	10/06/26	O	Ipswich Corporation.	No. 28. Strachan & Brown 30 seat body.
281	DX5631*	17/06/26	O	Ipswich Corporation.	No. 29. Strachan & Brown 30 seat body.
282	DX5632*	21/06/26	O	Ipswich Corporation.	No. 30. Strachan & Brown 30 seat body.
283	DX5633*	15/07/26	O	Ipswich Corporation.	No. 31. Strachan & Brown 30 seat body.
284	DX5634*	25/06/26	O	Ipswich Corporation.	No. 32. Strachan & Brown 30 seat body.
285	DX5635*	12/08/26	O	Ipswich Corporation.	No. 33. Strachan & Brown 30 seat body.
286	DX5636*	27/07/26	O	Ipswich Corporation.	No. 34. Strachan & Brown 30 seat body.
287	DX5637*	27/07/26	O	Ipswich Corporation.	No. 35. Strachan & Brown 30 seat body.
288				Ordered as demonstrator.	Order cancelled parts used in No. 300.
289		08/06/26	3½	Norwich Corporation.	No. 37 Chain driven. Kerbside control.
290		18/06/26	3½	Norwich Corporation.	No. 38 Chain driven. Kerbside control.
291		09/07/26	3½	Norwich Corporation.	No. 39 Chain driven. Kerbside control.
292		18/10/26	3½	Norwich Corporation.	No. 40 Chain driven. Kerbside control.
293		25/10/26	3½	Norwich Corporation.	No. 41 Chain driven. Kerbside control.
294		15/12/26	3½	Norwich Corporation.	Chain driven. Kerbside control.
295		18/12/26	3½	Norwich Corporation.	Chain driven. Kerbside control.
296			C	Not made	Ordered by Rangoon Electric Tramways.
297	KU9101	02/09/26	O	City of Bradford.	No. 532. Roe 37 seat body.
298	KU9102	06/09/26	O	City of Bradford.	No. 533. Roe 37 seat body.
299	KU9103	18/09/26	O	City of Bradford.	No. 534. Roe 37 seat body.
300	EE6461	22/07/26	O	Grimsby Corporation Tramways.	No. 1. Roe 36 seat body.
301	EE6462	30/07/26	O	Grimsby Corporation Tramways.	No. 2. Roe 36 seat body.
302	EE6463	30/09/26	O	Grimsby Corporation Tramways.	No. 3. Roe 36 seat body.
303	EE6464	24/09/26	O	Grimsby Corporation Tramways.	No. 4. Roe 36 seat body.
304	EE6465	30/09/26	O	Grimsby Corporation Tramways.	No. 5. Roe 36 seat body.
305				Not made.	
306	Export	04/08/26	O	NESA	No. 1. Strachan & Brown 20 seat body.
307	Export	16/08/26	O	NESA	No. 2. Strachan & Brown 20 seat body.
308	Export	27/08/26	O	NESA	No. 3. Strachan & Brown 20 seat body.
309	Export	10/09/26	O	NESA	No. 4. Strachan & Brown 20 seat body.
310	Export	22/09/26	O	NESA	No. 5. Strachan & Brown 20 seat body.

Works No	Reg No	Date	Type	Owner	Notes
311	NF311	02/10/26	GT	Manchester Corporation.	No. 20. Roe 36 seat body.
312	EF3370*	29/01/27	O	West Hartlepool Corporation.	No. 21. Roe 36 seat body.
313	EF3371*	09/02/27	O	West Hartlepool Corporation.	No. 22. Roe 36 seat body.
314	EF3372*	11/02/27	O	West Hartlepool Corporation.	No. 23. Roe 36 seat body.
315	EF3373*	11/02/27	O	West Hartlepool Corporation.	No. 24. Roe 36 seat body.
316	EF3374*	18/02/27	O	West Hartlepool Corporation.	No. 25. Roe 36 seat body.
317	EF3375*	22/02/27	O	West Hartlepool Corporation.	No. 26. Roe 36 seat body.
318	EF3376*	25/02/27	O	West Hartlepool Corporation.	No. 27. Roe 36 seat body.
319	EF3377*	01/03/27	O	West Hartlepool Corporation.	No. 28. Roe 36 seat body.
320	EF3378*	04/03/27	O	West Hartlepool Corporation.	No. 29. Roe 36 seat body.
321	EF3379*	10/03/27	O	West Hartlepool Corporation.	No. 30. Roe 36 seat body.
322	EF3380*	10/03/27	O	West Hartlepool Corporation.	No. 31. Roe 36 seat body.
323	EF3381*	15/03/27	O	West Hartlepool Corporation.	No. 1
324	GD6184	25/02/27	GTZ	Glasgow Corporation.	No. 537. Roe 30 seat body.
325	KW204	31/05/27	O	City of Bradford.	No. 538. Roe 30 seat body.
326	KW205	03/06/27	O	City of Bradford.	No. 539. Roe 30 seat body.
327	KW206	10/06/27	O	City of Bradford.	No. 1, RS&J 36 seat body.
328	DJ3243	09/05/27	O	St. Helens Corporation.	No. 3, RS&J 36 seat body.
329	DJ3245	31/05/27	O	St. Helens Corporation.	No. 4, RS&J 36 seat body.
330	DJ3246	18/05/27	O	St. Helens Corporation.	No. 2, RS&J 36 seat body.
331	DJ3244	25/05/27	O	St. Helens Corporation.	No. 6. Roe 36 seat body.
332	EE7097	29/04/27	O	Grimsby Corporation Tramways.	No. 7. Roe 36 seat body.
333	EE7098	24/05/27	O	Grimsby Corporation Tramways.	35 seater body. Order cancelled.
334			O	Ordered as demonstrator. Not made.	No. 6.
335	Export	27/06/27	O	NESA	No. 7.
336	Export	19/07/27	O	NESA	No. 8.
337	Export	19/07/27	O	NESA	No. 1.Roe 30 seat body.
338	Export	07/10/27	O	Imprese Electriche. (Lima Tramways)	No. 2.Roe 30 seat body.
339	Export	12/10/27	O	Imprese Electriche. (Lima Tramways)	No. 3.Roe 30 seat body.
340	Export	19/10/27	O	Imprese Electriche. (Lima Tramways)	No. 4.Roe 30 seat body.
341	Export	25/10/27	O	Imprese Electriche. (Lima Tramways)	No. 5.Roe 30 seat body.
342	Export	03/11/27	O	Imprese Electriche. (Lima Tramways)	No. 6.Roe 30 seat body.
343	Export	07/11/27	O	Imprese Electriche. (Lima Tramways)	No. 2
344	GD9154	22/12/27	GTZ	Glasgow Corporation.	No. 3
345	GD9155	31/12/27	GTZ	Glasgow Corporation.	No. 4
346	GD9156	31/12/27	GTZ	Glasgow Corporation.	No. 5
347	GD9157	07/01/28	GTZ	Glasgow Corporation.	No. 6
348	GD9158	12/01/28	GTZ	Glasgow Corporation.	No. 7
349	GD9159	18/01/28	GTZ	Glasgow Corporation.	No. 8
350	GD9160	26/01/28	GTZ	Glasgow Corporation.	No. 9
351	GD9161	27/01/28	GTZ	Glasgow Corporation.	No. 10
352	GD9162	31/01/28	GTZ	Glasgow Corporation.	No. 11
353	GD9163	07/02/28	GTZ	Glasgow Corporation.	No. 12
354	GD9164	13/02/28	GTZ	Glasgow Corporation.	No. 13
355	GD9165	27/02/28	GTZ	Glasgow Corporation.	No. 14
356	GD9166	14/02/28	GTZ	Glasgow Corporation.	No. 15
357	GD9167	29/02/28	GTZ	Glasgow Corporation.	No. 16
358	GD9168	07/03/28	GTZ	Glasgow Corporation.	No. 17
359	GD9169	07/03/28	GTZ	Glasgow Corporation.	No. 18
360	GD9170	13/03/28	GTZ	Glasgow Corporation.	No. 19
361	GD9171	13/03/28	GTZ	Glasgow Corporation.	No. 20
362	GD9172	14/03/28	GTZ	Glasgow Corporation.	No. 21
363	GD9173	16/03/28	GTZ	Glasgow Corporation.	No. 22
364	GD9174	21/03/28	GTZ	Glasgow Corporation.	No. 23
365	GD9175	23/03/28	GTZ	Glasgow Corporation.	No. 24
366	GD9176	24/03/28	GTZ	Glasgow Corporation.	No. 25
367	GD9177	26/03/28	GTZ	Glasgow Corporation.	No. 26
368		28/03/28	GTZ	Glasgow Corporation.	No. 27
369		30/03/28	GTZ	Glasgow Corporation.	No. 28
370		31/03/28	GTZ	Glasgow Corporation.	No. 29
371		10/04/28	GTZ	Glasgow Corporation.	No. 30
372		10/04/28	GTZ	Glasgow Corporation.	No. 31
373		16/05/28	GTZ	Glasgow Corporation.	No. 32
374	GD9182	21/04/28	GTZ	Glasgow Corporation.	No. 33
375		25/04/28	GTZ	Glasgow Corporation.	No. 34
376		01/05/28	GTZ	Glasgow Corporation.	No. 35
377	GD9187	10/05/28	GTZ	Glasgow Corporation.	No. 36
378		16/05/28	GTZ	Glasgow Corporation.	No. 34. Garrett 32 seat body.
379	WW4688	31/12/27	O	Mexborough & Swinton Tramways.	No. 38. Garrett 32 seat body.
380	WW4692	03/03/28	O	Mexborough & Swinton Tramways.	No. 35. Garrett 32 seat body.
381	WW4689	03/02/28	O	Mexborough & Swinton Tramways.	No. 39. Garrett 32 seat body.
382	WW4693	08/03/28	O	Mexborough & Swinton Tramways.	No. 36. Garrett 32 seat body.
383	WW4690	11/02/28	O	Mexborough & Swinton Tramways.	No. 37. Garrett 32 seat body.
384	WW4691	24/02/28	O	Mexborough & Swinton Tramways.	No. 1. Roe 60 seater body.
385	DT821	27/01/28	OS	Doncaster Corporation Tramways.	No. 2. Roe 60 seater body.
386	DT822	06/03/28	OS	Doncaster Corporation Tramways.	No. 104
387	HJ7363	28/02/29	OS	Southend on Sea Corporation.	

Works No	Reg No	Date	Type	Owner	Notes
388	DT823	31/03/28	OS	Doncaster Corporation Tramways.	No. 3. Roe 60 seater body.
389	DT824	13/04/28	OS	Doncaster Corporation Tramways.	No. 4. Roe 60 seater body.
390	Export	20/07/28	C2	Automobile Electric Supply Co. (Cape) Ltd., SA.	
391		/28	E	Ordered by Automobile Electric Supply Co.	Renumbered 433
392			O	Continental Demonstrator	
	DX9610	24/11/31		Ipswich Corporation	No. 45. Converted from demonstrator, 30 seater.
393	WW7872	26/10/28	O	Mexborough & Swinton Tramways.	No. 40. Garrett 32 seat saloon body.
394	WW7873	26/10/28	O	Mexborough & Swinton Tramways.	No. 41. Garrett 32 seat saloon body.
395	WW7874	26/10/28	O	Mexborough & Swinton Tramways.	No. 42. Garrett 32 seat saloon body.
396	WW7875	31/10/28	O	Mexborough & Swinton Tramways.	No. 43. Garrett 32 seat saloon body.
397	WW7876	31/10/28	O	Mexborough & Swinton Tramways.	No. 44. Garrett 32 seat saloon body.
398	WW7877	31/10/28	O	Mexborough & Swinton Tramways.	No. 45. Garrett 32 seat saloon body.
399	WW7878	05/11/28	O	Mexborough & Swinton Tramways.	No. 46. Garrett 32 seat saloon body.
400	WW7879	05/11/28	O	Mexborough & Swinton Tramways.	No. 47. Garrett 32 seat saloon body.
401	WW7880	05/11/28	O	Mexborough & Swinton Tramways.	No. 48. Garrett 32 seat saloon body.
402	WW8790	09/02/29	O	Mexborough & Swinton Tramways.	No. 49. Garrett 32 seat saloon body.
403	WW8791	11/02/29	O	Mexborough & Swinton Tramways.	No. 50. Garrett 32 seat saloon body.
404	WW8792	12/02/29	O	Mexborough & Swinton Tramways.	No. 51. Garrett 32 seat saloon body.
405	WW8793	14/02/29	O	Mexborough & Swinton Tramways.	No. 52. Garrett 32 seat saloon body.
406	WW8794	23/02/29	O	Mexborough & Swinton Tramways.	No. 53. Garrett 32 seat saloon body.
407	WW8795	21/02/29	O	Mexborough & Swinton Tramways.	No. 54. Garrett 32 seat saloon body.
408	WW8796	20/02/29	O	Mexborough & Swinton Tramways.	No. 55. Garrett 32 seat saloon body.
409	WW8797	18/02/29	O	Mexborough & Swinton Tramways.	No. 56. Garrett 32 seat saloon body.
410	WW8798	25/02/29	O	Mexborough & Swinton Tramways.	No. 57. Garrett 32 seat saloon body.
411	WW8799	26/02/29	O	Mexborough & Swinton Tramways.	No. 58. Garrett 32 seat saloon body.
412	WW8800	28/02/29	O	Mexborough & Swinton Tramways.	No. 59. Garrett 32 seat saloon body.
413	WW8801	28/02/29	O	Mexborough & Swinton Tramways.	No. 60. Garrett 32 seat saloon body.
414	HJ8925	21/05/29	OS	Southend on Sea Corporation.	No. 105
415	HJ8926	24/05/29	OS	Southend on Sea Corporation.	No. 106
416	HJ8927	27/06/29	OS	Southend on Sea Corporation.	No. 107
417	HJ8928	29/07/29	OS	Southend on Sea Corporation.	No. 108
418	HJ8929	29/07/29	OS	Southend on Sea Corporation.	No. 109
419		29/06/29	GTZ	Glasgow Corporation.	No. 42 Blackpool Cleansing Conference.
420		28/07/29	GTZ	Glasgow Corporation.	No. 37
421		28/07/29	GTZ	Glasgow Corporation.	No. 38
422		28/07/29	GTZ	Glasgow Corporation.	No. 39
423		30/07/29	GTZ	Glasgow Corporation.	No. 40
424		30/07/29	GTZ	Glasgow Corporation.	No. 41
425	WX4440	14/06/30	O	Mexborough & Swinton Tramways.	No. 61. Garrett 32 seat saloon body.
426	WX4441	31/05/30	O	Mexborough & Swinton Tramways.	No. 62. Garrett 32 seat saloon body.
427	WX4442	31/05/30	O	Mexborough & Swinton Tramways.	No. 63. Garrett 32 seat saloon body.
428		21/06/30	GTZ	Glasgow Corporation.	No. 43
429		29/09/30	GTZ	Glasgow Corporation.	No. 44
430		29/09/30	GTZ	Glasgow Corporation.	No. 45
431		29/09/30	GTZ	Glasgow Corporation.	No. 46
432	XS2607	18/09/30	GTZ	Paisley Corporation.	No. 4
433		23/07/30	ET	City of St. Albans.	Originally.No. 391
434	XS2608	18/09/30	GTZ	Paisley Corporation.	No. 5
435	GG4177	31/07/31	GTZ	Glasgow Corporation.	No. 47
436		31/08/31	GTZ	Glasgow Corporation.	No. 48
437		31/08/31	GTZ	Glasgow Corporation.	No. 49
438		31/08/31	GTZ	Glasgow Corporation.	No. 50
439		03/03/33	GTZ	Glasgow Corporation.	No. 52
440		10/03/33	GTZ	Glasgow Corporation.	No. 53
441		22/01/34	GTZ	Glasgow Corporation.	No. 55
442		23/01/34	GTZ	Glasgow Corporation.	No. 56
443		28/02/35	GTZ	Glasgow Corporation.	Pneumatic Tyres
444		06/03/35	GTZ	Glasgow Corporation.	Pneumatic Tyres
445	YS503	08/03/35	GTZ	Glasgow Corporation.	No. 57 Pneumatic Tyres
446		14/01/36	GTZ	Glasgow Corporation.	Pneumatic Tyres
447		07/01/36	GTZ	Glasgow Corporation.	Pneumatic Tyres
448		31/12/35	GTZ	Glasgow Corporation.	Pneumatic Tyres
449		14/01/36	GTZ	Glasgow Corporation.	Pneumatic Tyres
450		06/03/37	GTZ	Glasgow Corporation.	Pneumatic Tyres
451		11/03/37	GTZ	Glasgow Corporation.	Pneumatic Tyres
452		18/03/37	GTZ	Glasgow Corporation.	Pneumatic Tyres
453		25/03/37	GTZ	Glasgow Corporation.	Pneumatic Tyres

Total number of electric vehicles: 343

Garrett Internal Combustion Engined Vehicles

35127		20/09/27	E type	Scottish Commercial Cars.	Garrett - Caledon. Shaft drive.
§		/27	G type	Stock.	Garrett - Caledon. Chain drive.
§		/27	Freighter	RG&S Works use	Garrett - Caledon.
35223		/28	COW	Demonstrator	Prototype 6 wheel crude oil wagon.
	FL7345	01/11/28		Barford & Perkins, Peterborough.	
35224		/28	COW	Demonstrator	Prototype 4 wheel crude oil wagon.
	FL7344	01/11/28		Barford & Perkins, Peterborough.	
35455		7/31	GB6	Demonstrator	Blackstone engine.
		/32		A.Cork & Sons, Manchester.	
35466		6/31	GTZ diesel	Glasgow Corporation.	Blackstone engine.
35470		/31	GB6	Demonstrator	Blackstone and Aveling engines.
		09/06/32		Martin & Sillett, Strood, Kent.	Sold without engine.
35471		/31	GM6	Demonstrator	Meadows engine.
		09/06/32		Martin & Sillett, Strood, Kent.	Sold without engine.

Notes

§ Works serial numbers are not known to have been allocated to these vehicles.

Registration numbers are included where known. In cases where some uncertainty exists as to how the registration numbers carried by a particular fleet were related to chassis numbers, these are marked with an asterisk.

The abbreviation '*et*' denotes a tipper vehicle on the Garrett 'run back and tip' system. '*vet* ' denotes conventional vertical tipping gear for end tipping.

APPENDIX 6   Chronological Sequence of Events in the Building of Garrett Wagons

1905	First undertype steam wagon completed.
1907	Two examples of undertype steam wagon sold to South America.
1909	First 5-ton overtype steam wagon.
1911	First 3-ton overtype steam wagon.
1912	5-ton overtype revised design.
1916	First electric wagon.
1917	XL (*Suffolk Punch*) steam wagon built.
1919	Formation of AGE combine with Richard Garrett & Sons Ltd. as a wholly owned subsidiary.
1919	Production series of electric wagons begun in December.
1921	First QL undertype steam wagon.
1922/3	Tentative designs for petrol engined half-tracked truck.
1925	Trolley bus building begun.
1925	Manufacture of Caledon lorries taken over.
1925	Undertype steam wagon fitted with prototype poppet valve engine.
1926	6-ton overtype steam wagon launched.
1926	Prototype 6-wheeled undertype steam wagon.
1927	Last overtype wagon sold.
1927	First GTZ made.
1927	Production undertype steam wagon engines changed from piston valves to poppet valves. Restyled cab and revised driving position.
1927	First 6-wheeled trolley bus. (Shown at Olympia).
1928	First 6-wheeled undertype wagons sold.
1928	Crude oil wagons (COWS) made.
1928	First diesel engined tractor.
1929	First undertype 6-wheeled (*Suffolk Punch*) tractor.
1931	Diesel engined GTZ.
1931	GB6 diesel lorry made.
1931	First undertype wagon with pneumatic tyres.
1932	R.G. & S. in Receivership.
1932	Last steam wagon sold by Receiver.
1932	Richard Garrett Engineering Works Ltd. formed as subsidiary of Beyer Peacock & Co. Ltd.
1937	Last GTZ made.
1965	Last GTZ scrapped.
1981	Leiston Works finally closed.